A Handful of Toads

A Humorous Rural Tale

Lynnette Barlow

D1240901

ISBN 978-1-8382249-4-3

Cover design: Lynnette Barlow
Illustrations: Saffron, Lynnette, Philip, Natalia and Amelia.

Entertainment by: John Owen

Hampshire Oak
Publications

Published by Hampshire Oak Publications

A Handful of Toads

A Humorous Rural Tale

For Lucy

With thanks for all the support and encouragement.

Preface

Moving our young family from the busy south of England to become sheep farmers on the remote and beautiful 'sunshine Island' of Anglesey, or *Ynys Môn*, North Wales, sounded idyllic, the ultimate in 'no stress' country living. However, we were in for some surprises!

A Handful of Toads is set in the 1980s. All the tales told are based on real events and weave in the amusing side of farm, family and village life, while giving a respectful and entertaining insight into that delightful country and culture.

It is laced with historical events and issues surrounding that period that will be either familiar or educational, depending on the age and circumstance of the reader. It highlights the challenges to those who learned to integrate into the inimitable Welsh culture and commemorates our dear friends and family whose lives have been shaped by the experience.

Chapters

1 Into the Dark Unknown

Those first few nights in our new home were strange, so very quiet, as if crossing the Menai Straits was like slipping through a gateway in Time. No lorries thundered past the bedroom window, no bawdy pub songs drifted through the night at closing time. No neighbours chatted on the street corner, no need to draw the curtains. No fearless lollipop-man waited on the path outside in the mornings to leap courageously in front of roaring, clattering trucks so we could cross the road to get to school. In fact, no road, no sound - nothing!

I wondered again how I had managed to get myself talked into doing this. We had loved living in quaint medieval Wickham village with its attractive little shops and flower baskets hanging from every decorative lamppost. In the centre of the village square, grape vines overhang the courtyard of the Wine Bar, while the King's Head Inn, which once received gentry in horse-drawn coaches, holds history and mystery behind its wide, arched entrance. Chesapeake watermill, bedecked in aged wisteria,

1

stands as proudly as ever at the far end of the village since being built from the timbers of the Frigate USS Chesapeake, captured from the Americans during the war of 1812. The mill is served by the sparkling Meon River, which flows through the pretty villages of East and West Meon, Droxford, Wickham, on to Titchfield, then out into the Solent.

May Day fair held in Wickham square is the highlight of the year; the roads leading into the square are blocked off and gypsies come to camp in shiny chrome-covered caravans on every available roadside space. The gypsy horses are groomed, beribboned and tethered outside the Star Inn on the corner of the village square, and by tradition, one or two of them will receive a pint of beer *inside* the pub!

The air is filled with the rich smell of horse manure, and the sound of steel horseshoes clattering noisily on the tarmac as small buggies carrying excited children and their parents are whisked daintily up and down the Winchester Road. Red-faced owners puff and pant at the sides of the horses for sale as they are paraded at trotting pace along that busy thoroughfare. Loud and theatrical haggling over the price of the horses competes with the cheerful booming sounds of the funfair.

The excitement runs high as merrymakers come from miles around to join in the fun. Candyfloss and coconut shy, toffee apples and merry-go-rounds, dodgem cars and towering helter-skelter, waltzers and switchbacks, all cavort wildly through the memories of the weary but happy children as they drift homeward to bed. From our cottage near the corner of Wickham Square, we had been aware of the flashing lights and noisy chatter that continued long into the night - and the next day, they were all gone! Not a trace! Wickham village was again tranquil, serene and clean, as though Fair Day had all been a dream.

It had not been my life's ambition to live on Anglesey; it had happened instead as a consequence of lowered resistance. I had been in the glorious depths of decorating the very last room of our prettily renovated old cottage in colourful Laura Ashley wallpaper when the telephone rang. It was my father, calling from his new home in a quaint Welsh seaside village.

"Don't you worry about that little house anymore," he had said excitedly. "Your mother and I have found just what Philip has always wanted, a farmhouse with six acres for only £38,000!"

The paste brush and I had slumped into a sticky heap on the bottom stair and all my day's elation melted with me.

"But I don't want to live on Anglesey!" I wailed hopelessly, for I knew that Philip would not be able to resist.

"Just come up and look at the place" my Dad insisted; "you don't have to buy it if you don't like it, but I promise you will just love it!"

Thus, it happened that, as the lid was slowly closing on a warm and golden September day, we had found ourselves as a small convoy, weaving our way through the Hampshire villages, northward bound.

"Well, here we go, and it will be a good few hours before we finish this journey!" Philip had announced cheerfully as the trusty old Bedford Luton van, bulging with home and possessions, clanked and rumbled along the country roads. Snatched from her reverie his companion spun around to face him, the meaning of the comment being lost on her. Perhaps that was due to her fascination with the rapid passing of the little red brick houses nestling amongst the edges of the Bere forest, where soft lights were beginning to glow in their windows, although it was more likely because she was only four months old and a Jack Russell puppy at that. Either way, she was a contented little traveller that day and attempted a lunge-lick in Philip's direction but was restrained by the length of her lead, anchored to the passenger seat.

Poppy's story was one with a sad start but a happy outcome; she and her siblings were discovered in a black plastic sack, thrown into a ditch alongside the main road. Poppy had a downy white coat with patches of black and tan and an enormous personality. From the moment she first pattered confidently into the house with a presence that filled the room, we knew this little addition to our family would be very entertaining.

Philip frowned and rubbed at his beard, a habit he had when thinking or planning; he was pleased to be on his way at last, after all the months of negotiation and anxiety preceding the sale of our cottage. His vivid blue eyes danced as they followed the movements of his nineteen-foot Drascombe Lugger sailing boat that swayed restlessly ahead. He hoped his brother Paul would cope with towing the boat safely during the long journey; it was Philip's new 'toy', a luxury he had long awaited. With the boat and a smallholding in North Wales, his dreams were becoming a reality.

"Look at the swans on the lake!" Daniel bounced excitedly on his seat and pointed at the greying vision of Bishops Waltham palace, beneath which graceful gliding silhouettes cast rippling shadows. Amelia and Joshua giggled happily in their makeshift beds beside me in the back of the microbus that towed Philp's boat. Long after his younger brother and sister had succumbed to sleep, Daniel still watched through the bus window, his little curly head outlined against the silvering clouds, which draped wispily as calico across the moon-bathed night sky. Although he was only eight, nothing passed him by without intelligent scrutiny.

'We will soon settle in Wales and adapt to a new kind of life,' I kept telling myself as the profusion of Hampshire's trees began to thin, giving way to more open countryside, and our little red-brick

4

cottage fell further and further behind us. I asked myself the same questions I had asked these last few months of hectic preparation: 'Why am I doing this? I'm a southern-born 'townie'; will I ever adjust to country life in wild and windy Anglesey?'

Philip's brother, Paul, was in good spirits that evening, although he had been itching to get our small convoy on the road all day. We had been staying at his mother's house since the sale of our cottage, so when we had packed the last item firmly into the van and locked the last door on the house he was like a dog let off the leash! He steered the microbus through the narrow country lanes with all the expertise of an experienced trucker. That experience he had gained through his work as the driver for a street-lighting team; many streetlamps had Paul's team planted all over Hampshire.

His mother smiled at him quietly from the front passenger seat, as she hugged her faithful doggy companion, Emmie, more securely on her lap. She felt a surge of pride at his capability, he was the youngest son of her six children, and Philip was her second son. At least she knew that Paul would return home with her after this journey, if only for a few weeks until he finished his work contract. Then he would also move to Anglesey to join my sister Candy and their children in their new bungalow overlooking the Irish Sea. Lucy was bewildered by the decision of her two sons to uproot from their native Hampshire to travel hundreds of miles north to a 'foreign land' where she had heard were very few trees, an abundance of snakes and constant gale force winds. Nonetheless, here she was, as supportive a mother as ever, even though she was so disappointed to be losing her family to the wild unknown, so far away.

'Anglesey! Why Anglesey?' she had asked herself frequently as she had driven around on her daily work routine as District Nurse. She could understand their wanting the country life; had they not been used to such a life all their childhood? True, it had been difficult living as they did in such seclusion and with primitive amenities inside the boundaries of Knowle hospital, where she and her husband, Michael had both worked as nurses for the mentally disabled. Although money had always been tight, their six exuberant children had enjoyed the freedom of living in the countryside. They had spent every non-school moment climbing trees, running through the meadows or playing in the glistening Meon River, which ran clear, constant and trout-laden past their one hundred and fifty-year-old cottage near Old Funtley Mill.

Since the family had moved out, the cottage had become derelict. The vegetable garden, where the chickens once scratched, was now a tangle of weeds and Rastus, the smelly Billy goat, no longer foraged amongst the abundant herbage. The currant bushes in Philip's little soft fruit orchard now struggled hopelessly to survive the choke of nettles, brambles and ivy, and the red brick 'Fairy House', or the outside toilet, was now decorated in its entirety with a mass of 'Old Man's Beard'. The cottage, along with its surrounding land, had recently been sold privately, as had most of the rest of the grounds of Knowle hospital. Barbed wire fences and 'Keep Off!' signs had sprung up magically, forbidding entrance to former blackberry pickers, mushroom gatherers and country walkers.

Beyond Knowle, the local countryside was becoming swallowed up by the spread of bustling suburbia. Where once had sprawled strawberry fields and open meadows, now sprung up acre upon acre of tightly packed dwellings, each perched on a tiny, landscaped plot and each being a clone of its immaculate, expensive neighbour. Where once had run happy, tousle-haired children, smeared with the grime of a good day's play, a new breed of young people now appeared, streetwise and clad in designer clothing.

Reminiscing on that arduous night's journey to our new address, I remembered that awful moment when my mother-in-law had first alerted us to a problem with the van.

"Is everything all right?" I had heard her question Paul.

"Yes, yes, everything's fine," he had replied.

"Then why are you pumping the foot brake?" she persisted. Paul did not answer, but he was gripping the steering wheel hard, and from his reflection in the rear-view mirror, I could see the tension in his face. A faint smell of smoke wafted from the rear of the bus, while the light knocking noise I had noticed earlier was growing stronger. I had not paid too much attention to the sound as, although we had only had the bus for a few days, it was thoroughly serviced before our journey, so I dismissed knocking noises and smoky smells as new parts being 'worn in'. We coasted into a layby, and Paul yanked at the handbrake, bringing the vehicle to a halt.

"No brakes!" he had exclaimed with a relieved smile, his forehead glistening from the anxiety.

"Why didn't you tell us?" gasped Lucy as he threw open the door and leapt out.

"No point in us all being worried!" he grinned reassuringly before striding off to investigate. Lucy and I exchanged horrified glances. Just then, the headlights on Philip's van appeared in the rear-view mirrors as he pulled off the road into the layby behind us.

"Good grief! The wheel is on fire!" Philip's shocked voice came from the rear of the van. Lucy was out of the car door in an instant, holding Emmie tightly by the collar, while Daniel followed quickly behind them. Philip dived in and rummaged under the seat for the fire extinguisher, and then a loud 'hissing' noise came from outside. I hastily grabbed the two sleeping little ones and put them on the front seat, from where Paul swiftly lifted them to the safety of the grassy bank while I followed rapidly behind.

As we watched Philip's efforts anxiously from a safe distance, the smoke began to die down and stop; however, the intense heat of the brake drum soon caused the flames to burst back to life. Plunging back inside the bus, he re-emerged with a bottle of fizzy orange drink, shook it vigorously, and sprayed the contents over the rising flames. Again, the blaze subsided, but it revived with ferocity almost instantly! The extinguisher was empty, the bottle drained, and the fire was winning the battle. So, without a moment's hesitation and in true country-boy fashion, Philip resorted to the only natural resource available. He peed on it!

"Ah! That's done it!" we heard him say from our recess and returned our modestly averted gaze. However, our hopes were soon dashed as the inferno forcefully reappeared!

"Now, what shall we do?" Paul asked, shrugging his shoulders with an air of defeat. Looking up, he saw all of us staring expectantly at him, the flicker of lights from the passing traffic revealing contorting expressions on his face as realization steadily dawned as to what was expected of him.

Lucy and I found something 'of great interest' in the shadowy hedgerow to distract our attention, and we were still trying to interest the children in the same direction while their Uncle Paul 'performed' when we were surprised to hear a sudden and prolonged 'whooshing' sound! It was of such intensity that we abandoned modesty and spun around to witness the most astonishing sight - a man and his fire extinguisher in an AA Roadside Recovery overall!

Philip and I had a crucial appointment in Amlwch, Anglesey, at 10 am the following morning to sign the final papers for the house. So we all agreed that we should travel together in the two-seater van that night to Anglesey, where my worried parents would be waiting for us all. The last we saw of our dear little family that night was the children giggling together as Granny made makeshift tents out of their blankets on the bank at the side of the layby and fed them the picnic she had prepared before leaving home. Paul stood sentry as they settled down to wait for the tow truck to arrive and transport the microbus to its destination. I am eternally grateful for their love and support.

We did not sleep a wink that night; as the hours ticked by, every car headlight shining on the bedroom window at my parent's home aroused hope and expectation. As the sun rose on Cemaes Bay, Herring gulls glided over the village, 'yelping' the classic welcoming call of the seaside. They settled on the chimney pots of the row of cottages edging the little road that descended to the bay, where the waves rolled onto the beach and splashed against the harbour wall. What a relief to see the tow truck pull into Tudor-Royal at mid-day,  carrying our tired and bedraggled family. It had been a difficult night and a long journey, but all's well that ends well, so they say. Our family was safe, we had successfully finalized the purchase of our new farm, and we were ready to start a new life.

2 Autumn Terrors

Our new home, *Tŷ'n Llain,* had been very well maintained and cherished; the walls inside were white, the walls outside were white, the sun was white, and even the farm cat we had inherited was white. It was a different, dazzling, but cold light, a no-nonsense new world.

The original part of the house was a traditional two-up, two-down, stone-built Welsh cottage, about one hundred and forty years old, with low ceilings, walls two and a half feet thick and windows set on the outside of the deep windowsills. The fact that the only windows in that part of the house were all facing toward the east was a circumstance that we did not initially take note of; however, the reason was to become apparent in due time. By contrast, the kitchen extension with a bedroom above had large windows that allowed stunning views of the countryside to the north and west.

Having purchased an additional nine acres, we were now owners of a fifteen-acre farm, almost at the top of the rocky mountain terrain, known as Mynydd Mechell, with only a handful of peripheral neighbours and an unpaved half-mile track linking us with the rest of the world. But what a world! From our vantage point, we had panoramic views that swept down across a peppering of small farms and sparsely populated villages, set amongst rugged and gorse-strewn rocky outcrops. Disused windmills, devoid of their once glorious sails, stood like oversized milestones along the winding roads leading to the seaside fishing village of Cemaes Bay.

In the distance, enormous ocean-going freighters glinted in the sunlight beyond the grass-thatched cliffs as they glided past the mouth of the bay on their voyages to and from the busy

Merseyside harbours of Liverpool and Ellesmere Port. The Irish Sea melted into the endless sky; its boundary secrets disclosed only on occasion by the hazy glimpse of the distant Isle of Man or the mountains of Cumbria.

Within a little while, I began to warm to my new surroundings. The sun would creep over the crest of the mountain in the mornings, giving identity to the small groups of sheep grazing on the neighbours' fields in the distance. Then the cool, bright whiteness of a Welsh September morning would slide in through the window, welcoming us to life and a new day.

Arthur and Dilys from *Pencae* near the entrance to our land were pleased to make our acquaintance as we passed the gate leading to their farmhouse. The quiet but friendly retired couple grazed just a handful of sheep on their well-manicured, rolling lawns and owned a dog named Gel, short for Gelert, the faithful hound of Llewelyn the Great, a medieval Welsh prince. Arthur was pleased to show Philip his immaculately organised, well-equipped workshop with a forge, milling machine, lathe and pillar drills. He was an artisan in all kinds of metalwork, a skill that Philip would call upon from time to time over the years.

With the tranquil atmosphere of *Tŷ'n Llain*, I began to revive memories of life as a child. When we moved into our brand-new council house in the South East of England during the 1950s, the garden was carved out of the swaying wheat fields, which swept down the valley to the broad, tidal River Medway. The historic city of Rochester, with its ancient castle, stood just across on the other side of the river, while away into the distance rolled the entrancing greens of the North Downs countryside of Burham and Wouldham. Quite rapidly, however, our wheat fields were transformed into endless streets and residences with only a few acres of fields and scrubland remaining where Gypsies kept their horses and where the locals cultivated productive allotments. My three sisters and I would spend the long, hot summer days there, running amongst the sweet meadow flowers with our friends or burrowing through the hawthorns and thickets to create our dens. We formed gangs, girls against boys and made many unsuccessful attempts at mounting the stocky horses with their ungainly bald patches and wart-ridden knees. That had been our world; we had no fears, and vehicles were scarce, with bus or bicycle being the alternative means of transport to 'Shanks' pony' (or walking).

One sad day, however, the men came with their diggers, ripped up our dens, and our playground soon became another housing estate; even the woods at the far end of the road were gradually swallowed up by invasive suburbia. Then suddenly, the rhythmic puffs of white steam marking the train line along the Medway valley disappeared as the steam trains were replaced by more modern diesel trains. Therefore, here at *Tŷ'n Llain*, I realized, was a second chance to enjoy the delights of my childhood. Here were the pretty wildflowers I had stashed in the back of my memory; here were the meadows, ripe and ready for three exuberant children to run through and live life as children should. Here the air was like champagne, as the previous owner, Jean Crutchley,

13

Amelia

had said when she reluctantly handed over ownership of her beloved home.

The fields of *Tŷ'n Llain* had been untouched by herbicide or chemical fertiliser, resulting in many varieties of wildflowers, which had appealed to Philip when we first visited the farm the previous April. Stan Crutchley had permitted the neighbouring farmers to take a single cut of summer hay from the fields each year, but for the rest of the year, he had kept only a couple of donkeys to eat down the remaining growth of late summer and autumn.

The old donkey shed was made partly from corrugated iron, built against a ten-foot-high irregular-shaped rock, which jutted vertically on one side to form one of the walls. It was there that little Joshua learned his love of rock climbing; he would stand triumphantly on the rusty corrugated roof of the shed, much to his mother's alarm. It did not take long for Philip to dismantle the donkey shed for safety reasons, but that did not quell Joshua's ardour for rock climbing, and he even persuaded Amelia to join him in his newfound sport. Peering from a bedroom window one day, I spotted two tiny figures away in the distance, holding hands and rock-hopping happily along the boundary of our land. Our little ones had never known such freedom, and at that moment, I felt that all the changes we had made would be worthwhile.

Philip was in his element; like a caged animal released back to the wild, his changed situation aroused in him a zest for life that had been suppressed over recent years. I had been surprised and delighted when early in our courtship he had bounded over a wire fence to gather a cluster of primroses from the woods for me. I knew then that life with Philip would never be 'run of the mill'; he was a country boy through and through. Watching him working with tireless enthusiasm on the farm made me aware of the sacrifices he had made for the previous ten years of our marriage to indulge my need for urban life.

As the weeks passed, the house began to look more like 'home' with our personal effects dotted around and the windows framed with ill-matched curtains we had brought from our previous cottage in Wickham. Precious photographs and artistic works decorated the walls while bunches of wildflowers especially picked for Mummy, sat in every vase. The days were still warm, bright and sunny, a breath of summer in the middle of autumn. I began to relax, deeming it a myth that Anglesey was continuously battered by strong winds, a malicious slander against this tranquil Isle!

It had been a month of discovery for the family, getting to know our neighbours and surroundings. We had been introduced to Jeffrey horse, the mean-tempered Shetland pony living in the neighbouring field belonging to *Bryn Llyn*, meaning 'Hill by the Lake'. *Bryn Llyn* was a converted cowshed; its occupants, Haydn and Alwyn Tudbull, were a very kind and hospitable elderly couple and the parents of Jean Crutchley, the previous owner of our house. That explained the well-worn, daisy-embedded track established through the long grass between the two properties.

The little gate to *Bryn Llyn* was readily opened to us as we bore gifts of home bakes and wildflower bouquets. Weaving our way through the dark and narrow passageways of their humble home, we would know exactly where to find Haydn; he would be sitting in the 'parlour' by the hearth of a small fireplace, where Alwyn would leave us while she went to the kitchen to fetch some tea and biscuits. Haydn had fallen into the hold of the cargo ship he was working on almost fifty years earlier during the Second World War and had seriously injured his back. He had lived and moved with increasing daily pain ever since, while Alwyn was his constant and caring nurse and attendant.

Their son, Leslie, and his wife, Heulwen, lived in a caravan in the back garden and in all the years that we lived in *Tŷ'n Llain*, I never once saw Leslie without his flat cap. Like the tweed jacket he wore for all occasions, the pattern on the cap had become indiscernible with age and use. He was an amiable, but shy and reclusive man, always smiling or chuckling, but it took a lot of concentration to get the gist of his conversations. Most of his interjections sounded like 'Doo', which we later discovered to mean, *Duw*, the Welsh word for 'God'. Leslie was a trained plumber, but he had been unemployed for a very long time.

"I was born in South Wales but they only give the work to North Walians here. Doo!" he said sadly. We wished we had known that before.

We soon came to befriend some English families with children of similar ages to our own; some came from the south of England and some from various parts of the north of England. Never had I been made so aware of the extreme differences in accents and contortions of the English language; I felt I would more easily understand Chinese than I did some of those Northern English accents!

The Mackenzie family was one of the families with whom we formed a colourful relationship. Carl was an affable, energetic character from Newcastle, while Sandra was an objective and well-organized mother who took her husband's enthusiasm for life in her stride. She was an artist whose talents showed themselves in the decor of her home and the presentation of her family.

"Ah poot ma boot ina wadda yesserdee!" Carl said proudly in his strong Geordie accent when we next called to visit them in their attractive cottage in Cemlyn. "Do you wanna coom oot en try id oot wimme sumtime?" he asked Philip.

"I would like to see your boat, Carl," Philip replied cautiously; he had always liked boats, having owned several over the years. He had also been well-trained in the skill of sailing and maritime protocol by his father, a former member of the Royal Navy Sailing Association and instructor for the RN Sea Cadets. However, one thing Philip had learned from personal experience was the need to be sure of the seaworthiness of the vessel and the competence of the skipper before embarking on any voyage.

Having enjoyed a mellow and pleasant September in our new home, we were wondering what to expect next of autumn on the run down to winter. We had not thought to ask when we decided to buy *Tŷ'n Llain*, what was the purpose of the rough spread of concrete covering the roof slates or the reason for the large concrete blocks sitting on top of the metal cover to the coal bunker. That was a big mistake!

One evening, as our family sat around our antique walnut table, enjoying an evening meal together, we became aware of a faint and foreign sound from somewhere in the distance. We all paused in mid-munch and looked at each other across the table, trying to discern the cause of this strange new noise. Could it be a low-flying fleet of aircraft heading toward us? Perhaps it was a large herd of elephants trumpeting as they marched our way? Whatever it was, it was an unearthly, sinister and menacing sound.

The TV aerial on the roof, secured by a sturdy aluminium tube, began to sing with the undulating harmonics of a Peruvian flute, and some of the children's toys left outside suddenly shot past the window. We heard a loud thud as the heavy metal lid of the coal bunker was lifted from its seating and hurled into the vegetable garden. The noise intensified, becoming a vicious shrieking, which whirled around the house like a furious *banshee*, while the roof slates chattered with the resonance of an out-of-tune piano. The windows bowed inward with an unseen force, magnifying and distorting the reflection of our shocked and bewildered faces like fairground mirrors. Within a short while, we realized we were under the harsh, sudden, and powerful attack of what we came to know as the Westerly winds of Anglesey!

The next morning the weather was sunny and tranquil, like a petulant child awakening from a deep, blissful sleep after having gone to bed in a tantrum, with no trace of remorse for its behaviour of the previous evening. As we crept cautiously downstairs for breakfast, we all felt disturbed and traumatised by that first windstorm, and none of us felt well-rested after a tense night of meteorological terrorisation. The telephone rang, and everyone jumped in alarm, knocking over teacups and spilling breakfast cereal across the table.

"Philip, it's Carl, I need yur halp!" Carl's voice on the telephone sounded urgent.

"I will be there, Carl; I will come right now," Philip replied. We were all staring at him as he replaced the telephone on the wall bracket in the hallway and told us about Carl's dilemma. "Carl needs help to get his boat up out of the water; it is being smashed by the waves and he cannot manage it by himself." He took a large gulp of tea and disappeared out of the back door.

Twenty minutes later, Philip sped past the high walls of *Bryn Aber*, Cemlyn Bay, which was once the home of the reclusive pioneer aviator Captain Vivian Hewitt. He swung the Microbus into the car park next to Carl's old blue Volvo Estate and raced up the well-worn track, past an ancient tumbledown stone-built house to the pebbly beach of the bay. Philip was shocked at the sight before him; although the wind had abated inland, it was still causing havoc out to sea, and the monstrous ocean swell crashed repeatedly onto the craggy shore of Cemlyn Head. It swirled menacingly into Cemlyn Bay, where the waves were like large brutish thugs, damaging everything in their path with cruel relish!

Carl was striding up and down the beach, knee-deep in the buff-coloured foam, whipped up and blown inland. He looked justifiably distraught, tormented and helpless; his treasured boat was just a mass of broken planks tossed up in the surf but tauntingly just out of reach. It was evident that one step too close and that powerful sea would also have him in its merciless grasp. It was a very frightening sight! Poor Carl; local knowledge could have helped him to know he should not have put his boat in the water just there, but like us, he was still new to the area and unfamiliar with the power of the wind and waves on Anglesey. Carl returned miserably to Cemlyn, while Philip drove down to the little grocery store in Cemaes Bay and met Carl at his home, armed with a bottle of whisky, which they shared in mutual commiseration.

As October progressed, the frequent autumn winds caused us to become irritable with the daily battle when we needed to go outside; like an invisible enemy, it was impossible to challenge or hide from it. On a visit to the Mackenzie family one evening, a sudden, fierce gust of wind wrenched little Joshua from my hand and hurled him across the road into a hawthorn hedge. The Great Black-Backed Seagulls sought inland shelter but could not make

headway in the windstorms. Daniel and Joshua found it most amusing to watch as the gulls appeared to fly *backwards* past the windows. Hanging the washing out on the line, with the collar of my coat whipping against my face was a real endurance; however, Amelia was fascinated with the way the cleaned clothes danced energetically on the washing line all by themselves. On the positive side, by the time I had finished hanging out the laundry at one end of the line, the clothes on the other end were virtually dry and ready to bring back indoors; provided they managed to cling to the line despite their battle with that mischievous wind.

However, an even more significant meteorological event assailed the southern part of England that we had just left behind. It was the night of 15-16 of October 1987, and we were expecting Philip's brother, Paul, to travel up from Hampshire. While my sister, Candy, and their children waited anxiously for him in their bungalow, *Saith Môr*, on the clifftops of Amlwch, the morning news gave the shocking report of a violent cyclone, which had occurred overnight. Hurricane-force winds, with gusts of around 135 mph. had reportedly swept across some of the northern regions of France and the Channel Islands, a speed experienced only once in two hundred years! The south and south-eastern areas of England suffered enormous damage as the cyclone continued on its way towards the North Sea. We heard that schools were closed and forests, parks, roads and railways were strewn with fallen trees. Thousands of homes were without electricity, and tragically at least 22 people were killed during that storm in England and France alone. It was estimated that 15 million trees were brought down throughout the affected parts of England that night. Many were destroyed in the parks of London, while our beloved forest, Bedgebury Pinetum in Kent, lost a quarter of its trees overnight. Six of the seven oaks in the town of Sevenoaks that had graced the edge of the cricket pitch since the turn of the century were uprooted; so Sevenoaks suddenly became a sad 'One Oak'.

To our amazement, the following afternoon, we received a telephone call from Paul to say he had arrived safely in Amlwch, with no incidents.

"We did not think you would come today!" I exclaimed. "How did you possibly manage the journey without getting hurt? Weren't trees falling onto the roads?"

"Oh yes," Paul replied nonchalantly in his unfazed manner. "They were falling all around me, but I just drove around them and kept going."

The weather predictions and warnings for that storm appear to have been so lightly addressed, and even inaccurate, which became a bone of contention over which Britain chewed for decades.

"Earlier today a woman rang the BBC and said she heard there was a hurricane on the way. Well, if you are watching, don't worry, there isn't," one TV weather forecaster assured derisively. However, not even the strongest weather warning could have prepared Europe for the sudden, monstrous attack of the 'Great Storm' that struck on the night of October 15th 1987!

On a later journey to Hampshire, we were amazed to see that not only had many trees been uprooted but some stout oaks were snapped in half! Philip grieved for the loss of one of his tree friends, where he had found comfort among its branches during childhood, and he was moved to write a poem of lament.

The Hampshire Oak

By Philip Barlow

Today I went to pay my respects to a special friend
And there he lay with his big bones bleached by the sun
Lifeless and fallen, lying down the hill, dry roots in the air.
His days of dignity long gone, with no hope of mend.
Rugged bark peeled away, poor old chap, quite undone.
With a heart full of sadness, I just stand and stare.

Former days, with glory clothed, arms thrust toward the sky
All around, Wood Anemones and Violets grew in patches.
Autumn harvesters into their stash, acorns they shove.
You nurtured them all, squirrel, jay, moth and butterfly.
Though decked in leaves, ne'er mentioned in dispatches,
Strong, stout trunk, linking the earth with heaven above.

In times of old, wise craftsmen would spare a thought.
King George a silver thruppence your image did mint.
Many a barn roof, with rafter, beam and purlins did grace.
Safe and secure below decks, Jack Tar in Victory's port,
Half-timbered buildings with wattle, daub, thatch and flint.
Into your arms, a boy climbed for comforting embrace.

As I reflect on the passing of my cherished friend,
I know also that my days of glory will one day end.

3 The Rayburn

The house was getting quite cold at night by November, especially in the kitchen and bedroom extension that had been added to the gable end of the original house some fifteen years earlier, with no insulation built into its thin walls. My sister, Terrie, made the helpful suggestion of fitting a Rayburn stove in the kitchen, which appealed to us, so we found a fair-priced supplier in Kidderminster.

Having ascertained the measurements of the proposed cooker, Philip then drew sketchy lines on the floor and started to create the raised stone slab hearth to house it. Meanwhile, the children and I were enlisted to go out into the fields to source some flat and decorative slabs to go on the top. It was an enjoyable task, the children were happy to do something fun and useful to contribute to the cause, while watched closely by Dinky-Doo the farm cat, who was hoping to catch a tasty meal of any mice running out from underneath the stones.

Next, with a neat circle of precise proportions scribed upon the kitchen wall, Philip set to work purposefully with his masonry drill to create a hole for the flue to access the original chimney. Unfortunately, the small hole, the size of a tea plate, that Philip had envisaged was growing extensively and he realized the place where the flue needed to enter the wall was not just a stone, but one enormous boulder! It was hard to gauge its size, due to the rendering on the kitchen wall, so he found it necessary to access the chimney via the bathroom wall on the other side. From where he stood in the bath with the plaster chipped off the wall, he was able to get a better idea of what he was dealing with, eventually being able to evict the colossus, leaving a misshapen cavern that could have housed a small elephant!

Using a rickety old wooden ladder, Philip then climbed cautiously onto the roof. The bowed ridge on the original part of the cottage gave away its age, while the smearing of concrete across both rooftops told the story of their battle against the fearsome elements. Thankfully, that day was a mild, windless day, soothingly quiet and peaceful. Judging carefully, he decided it was the concreted cap on the left chimney flue that needed removing with the deft use of his four-pound club hammer. That turned out to be the wrong choice he discovered, after a precarious descent back down to the kitchen. The chimney-sweeping brush jammed

against the concrete cover on the right-hand chimney flue, meaning another scary climb up the unsteady ladder and another mighty swing of the club hammer.

Hopeful of success this time, Philip took a few moments to view the world from the rooftop. It was a stunning view, which he would have enjoyed spending longer looking at if the work at hand had not been so pressing and if he had not had such a fear of heights. The children and I watched anxiously from the back garden, as he very cautiously descended the ladder again. A few minutes later, a cheer went up as the brushes burst out successfully from the correct chimney pot this time, sending a spray of ancient soot and twiggy Jackdaw nests before it.

For the next two weeks, the gaping hole between the kitchen and bathroom was an amusing topic of conversation, as well as a source of considerable embarrassment. That was especially so for visitors who had popped in to share a *panad*, the local term for a cup of tea. Eventually, someone came up with the idea of stuffing the offending hole with some of Philip's biggest jumpers and several bath towels, which at least screened off the peep show.

Finally, the happy day came when Philip and his brother, Paul, set off to collect the Rayburn. It was considerably cheaper to buy the sable and brown one than the scarlet one that we would have preferred, and it saved a lot of money by their going to collect it themselves. Therefore, they left very early in the Microbus, as the drive to Kidderminster and back would take a whole day for the round trip. The Rayburn was made of enamel-coated cast iron and it was going to be heavy, so Philip had put out the call for help among our friends in readiness for its arrival.

When the men returned with their booty that evening, they were delighted to discover a couple of willing, robust volunteers already sitting at the kitchen table, enjoying tea and cake while waiting for them. How grateful they were for the support. With much grunting, groaning and conflicting instructions issuing from the back of the bus, the Rayburn, weighing in at more than eight hundred pounds, or three hundred and twenty kilos, came to settle, still on its pallet and enshrouded in its protective cardboard box, on the concrete path just outside the back door.

The back door! Now, there was a problem we had not previously considered. How were they to get one incredibly weighty Rayburn, surrounded by several helpful, hefty men through the slim back door? It was certainly time for another piece of cake, a cup of tea and a good think.

"One of us can come inside first and guide it in that way, with someone else on the outside to push," suggested Mark. Well, I think that was what he said; I did wonder how they understood each other, as Mark and Gary came from Manchester and to me, who was only used to the accents from around London, they might

25

just as well be speaking Gujarati. *Mancunian* was clearly a language I would need to learn if I were to get along with immigrants from the north of England.

Now though, how to lift the Rayburn over the doorstep was the pressing problem. Philip suddenly remembered the long, hollow metal pole he had found on a building site while he was doing fencing work in Hampshire, so he marched out purposefully to the old barn to collect it. At over six feet long, it had made the perfect shaft for his broken spade and one of his favourite tools for digging deep fence postholes. On this day it would prove to be invaluable. Someone volunteered a chunky towrope, which Mark and Gary fed through the pallet under the Rayburn, making two loops above it, through which was inserted the metal pole and then it was ready for lifting.

Since Paul and Philip were the strongest of the group, it made sense that they should be the ones to haul the pole up onto their shoulders. Bearing that heavy, swaying burden, they shuffled slowly and carefully in single file over the doorstep and through the back door. The strain on the faces of the two brothers, with the veins standing out on their arms, gave testimony to their challenging mission. However, step by step, with Gary providing guidance from inside the kitchen and Mark adding words of encouragement along with the odd one-finger push on Philip's back as his contribution from without, they managed to stumble across the threshold and place their weighty charge on the kitchen floor. There the valiant team were finally able to release the Rayburn from its towrope bondage and the children set to, excitedly ripping apart the cardboard box to reveal its soft coffee and beige hues. With one man on each corner, the Rayburn was finally lifted and gently settled on its prepared platform, solid, shiny and proud.

Success! Now, more than a cup of tea was in order. Yes, beers all around and a huge sandwich each to consolidate the day's efforts where cheerful, incomprehensible and self-congratulatory chatter around the old kitchen table finished off the episode nicely.

By the end of the week, Philip had connected the flue and the shiny copper pipes ready for the hot water and heating. He had filled the gaping hole in the wall with cement and stones collected from the fields and plastered and painted the walls. No more awkward conversations between the kitchen and bathroom.

Llew Jones, the coalman, came to deliver our first load of coal in the large, two-ton coal bunker. A tall, lean man was Llew Jones, who always wore a black leather jerkin over his cable-knit, navy pullover to protect his shoulders from the heavy coal sacks. He was constantly cheerful, with a positive outlook and an ever-present sparkle of mirth in his eyes to match the smile set into his coal-blackened face. From him, we were to learn all the local news and gossip as he shared a *panad* while leaning against the framework of our open kitchen door.

Driven on by increasingly chilly nights, Philip's next mission was to deal with the need for a hot water radiator system for heating the whole house. Our new friend, Ernie Taylor, from Stockport in Cheshire, a plumber by trade, became his much-appreciated advisor. Under Ernie's instructions, Philip was successfully able to construct the central heating system using the self-flowing, rising hot water and falling cold water gravity method, which worked without the use of electricity. This meant that, in the event of a power cut, the Rayburn cooker, the hot water and the heating system would all continue to work as good as gold.

Ernie supplied the reconditioned radiators for the job and all the bright copper piping to match those in the kitchen and he loaned Philip the necessary tools to do the job. He was a mild-mannered, humble man and we learned more about him over a *panad* and cake. One afternoon, he revealed to us a personal experience, making us aware that we were in the presence of a modest, unsung hero.

"We were living in a little terraced house in the middle of Stockport at the time; Kath was six months pregnant with our Ian," Ernie began to relate the most traumatic event of his life. "It was a Sunday morning, about ten o'clock and we were late getting up. I had just come down to the kitchen to put the kettle on the stove for a cup of coffee and was about to make some toast when I heard a tremendous roaring sound; it was frightening as if it was coming through the house! The whole place shook and Kath came quickly down the stairs looking as white as a sheet; we had no idea what it was. We looked out of the kitchen window overlooking Hope's Carr, where we could see black smoke rising." Everyone in our kitchen gasped as Ernie's story unfolded.

"When was this Ernie?" I asked.

"I remember it so clearly," Ernie replied, his gaze wandering out of the window as he recalled that shocking moment. "It was the 4th of June 1967," he continued and we were all raptly attentive.

"What did you do, Uncle Ernie?" Daniel asked, his eyes wide with anticipation.

"Well, I thought, 'this looks serious!' So, I switched off the gas under the kettle and ran across the road, just as I was, in my jeans, t-shirt and slippers. Going through an alley leading to an open area I could see the tailpiece of an aeroplane sticking out from the smoke."

"Oh, my goodness!" I gasped, enthralled by the account. Ernie was entranced as if he were reliving that painful memory.

"No one else was around when I got there, I could make out that the plane was broken up into three parts. The local policeman, Bill Oliver, came running over and we both quickly climbed into the open part of the plane to try to pull out any survivors."

"Were you able to save them all, Uncle Ernie?" Amelia asked, her little face flushed with concern.

"We managed to get four people out between us and then other neighbours came to help too, but it was getting so terribly hot inside the plane and the hair on my arms and face was getting burnt, so we had to stop. We backed off as far away as possible before the fuel in the tank under the plane exploded. I heard later that there were eighty-four people on board the plane," Ernie shook his head sadly, "but only twelve survived."

A shudder went down my back at the reality of a 'hands-on' experience, as related by this unassuming and gentle man.

"You must have been in shock after that, Ernie," I stated with feeling. "Were you alright? What did you do then?"

"The emergency services arrived quite quickly and there was nothing more I could do," Ernie replied, a frown creasing his brow with his troubled thoughts. "I was covered in blood and had a gash in my foot from standing on some jagged metal; someone thought I was one of the survivors, but I said I was all right and I limped home barefoot. I have no idea what happened to my slippers. Kath was praying on the doorstep when I got back home; she was worried out of her wits! I just threw my bloodstained clothes in the dustbin, bathed and stayed indoors for the rest of the day. I have hardly ever spoken of it since."

Ernie held his warm cup of tea between both hands and sat staring at the floor, while a thousand frantic and distressing sounds and memories charged painfully before him through the next few silent moments around the kitchen table. Daniel and Amelia stared open-mouthed at Ernie, while Joshua looked from one to the other of the adults, trying to understand why everyone had suddenly gone so quiet. We could tell there was so much more to his story than he was telling us, but for his sake and that of the children, we decided it was best not to probe.

"What an experience, Ernie!" Philip said gently, breaking the silence. He had heard of that disaster and, even though he was only twelve years old at the time, the event had impressed itself on his memory.

It was a tense moment when Philip's plumbing efforts were put to the test, but Ernie had been right about the 'gravity-flow' method of plumbing being effective without the use of electricity. After charging the system with water and lighting a small pile of coals in the Rayburn's firebox, the smoke wafted up the chimney and out of the new clay chimney pot with a good draught. When the air was 'bled' from the radiators, they started to bubble and rattle into life, then warmth began seeping into every corner of the old, cold stone house. An endless supply of hot water spurted from the taps, meaning luxuriously hot baths every night at little expense. With the cream-coloured enamel kettle whistling softly on the hotplate and the smell of dinner cooking in its oven, the kitchen began to radiate cosiness as the Rayburn became the warm and welcoming hub of the home.

It was while he was digging into the wall of the old parlour to route some pipes that Philip was surprised to find an unusually large old toad that must have been living in the stone wall for decades. It would have survived by feeding on the insects, such as woodlice and centipedes in the earth packed between the stones. The toad was now of enormous proportions, completely covering Philip's outsized hand. It blinked in bewilderment as he carefully carried it outside into the light to a shaded spot in the back garden.

The children gathered around and marvelled at the knobbly-backed creature, which, as Philip had explained, was probably extremely old, even older than their Mum and Dad.

"Don't kiss it, Mum!" Daniel chipped in cheekily. "No thanks Daniel, I did that once before," I replied. "Anyway, we already have quite enough handsome princes around here!" Philip shot me a quizzical glance as he lowered the creature to the ground close to the bushes. The toad moved off with stiff, slow, movements, leaving behind a wet deposit on his hand, which we later discovered toads are inclined to do in times of stress. Then it ambled unhurriedly into the undergrowth.

We never saw it again, but we hoped it would continue to live on for many more years in its liberated state. Maybe it would help us to keep on top of the slug and snail population, which was steadily decimating many of the plants in what had been a pretty garden when we first came to *Tŷ'n Llain.* How did it get to be there in the first place we wondered? Our neighbour 'who knows all things' was just the man to ask.

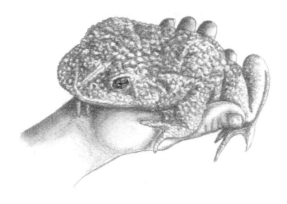

The Ancient Toad

By Lynnette Barlow

How did it get there?
That toad from of old.
A relic from yesteryear,
What tales could be told?

Did it spawn in the mire of Time?
Did it once writhe in the pond of its birth?
Was it uprooted by an ancient hand?
Was it then carried amongst clods of earth?

Packed into the wall
Between rocks large and fast,
Then covered in plaster
As a new home was cast

One hundred plus years
In a mud-packed wall,
So large and stiff
It could scarcely crawl.

Aged and enormous
With insects replete,
It blinked at the sunlight,
Felt the turf at its feet.

It lurched back to the meadow
A free toad at last,
A wart-ridden reminder
Of an era, that's passed

4 The Oracle

We soon came to realize that the lane leading to our house was an infrequently used ancient public footpath, which led past the front door, over a stone stile and down into a marsh that was only accessible during the dry periods of summer. This discovery accounted for the random apparitions, which glided past the kitchen window from time to time, without bothering to knock on the door. During the wet autumn and winter months of the year, when the marsh was inaccessible, the walkers were wont to pass through our field gate, over to our top fields and away to the summit of Mynydd Mechell by means of an all-season, parallel path. It was from this direction that we received a visit from our neighbour from *Bryn Awel*, a brick-built farm cottage at the other end of the original, prescribed boggy footpath.

John Owen loped down from our top fields one day, purposely to make our acquaintance. A tall, dark-haired, good-looking fellow, wearing a blue boiler suit over his slim frame, hobnail boots and the traditional flat cloth cap pulled firmly down on his head. Philip was sorting out the contents of the old barn and organizing the few scant tools we had brought with us from Hampshire when John loomed up behind him and greeted him in a jovial manner.

"What do you plan to do with the land?" he was interested to know.

"We thought of sheep," Philip replied. John Owen looked sceptical. "We've bought another nine acres from the previous owner," Philip added defensively, gesturing toward the rugged terrain that rose steeply from the other side of the field where Jeffrey the Shetland pony lived and from whence John had arrived. "And I believe there is a grant offered by the government for the fencing."

"*Arglwydd!* (Lord) You won't make a living out of sheep on

fifteen acres of land!" John stated candidly, eyeing the horizon where our top fields disappeared over the brow of the Mount.

"Maybe not," Philip replied, a little irritated by John's candour. "But I am hoping to supplement it by doing some contract gardening or find some work with local farmers." John Owen still looked sceptical.

"Do you have a good spade?" he asked, peering into the dark recesses of the old barn.

"Why do you ask?" Philip was surprised by such a bold question.

"Because sheep die!" stated John, fixing Philip with a sage and knowing expression, and how right he was, we were to discover. The next time he came to visit, he carried an old, solid garden spade and thrust it generously into Philip's hand in confirmation of his sinister predictions. John became a frequent visitor after that and during his time sitting at our kitchen table, enjoying a *panad*, we would hear many enlightening stories about the local people and customs. There were only about 300 metres between our homes, with a saucer-shaped valley between us that was open to *Llyn Bwch*, a small lake to the northwest. On the rare still day, Philip and John could have an audible conversation with each other across the valley, without even shouting. John was a notable fencing contractor and the self-nominated local oracle. He proved to be a shrewd and perceptive man, with a distinct air of rogue about him; anything needed, John Owen knew from where it could be sourced.

"No television?" he asked on one of his visits. We had not had a television for most of our married life; still, John insisted that a television was an essential commodity for the children in this latitude of the Northern hemisphere, to while away the long, dark winter nights. On his next visit, he delivered a small portable television, which the children received with rapt delight. So, we decided to 'page the local Oracle' and ask John about the old toad in the wall.

It was an unseasonably mild day in December when he sat with us at the wooden picnic table outside the back door.

"You see all those stones there?" John asked, waving his arm in a wide arc to take in the expanse of grassy pasture leading up to the top fields. It would have been hard *not* to notice all those stones there, as those irregular-shaped, lichen-covered grey rocks made up the basis for all the walls between each field. They were scattered randomly as decorative features throughout the pasture wherever one looked and they formed most of the houses and barns in the area.

"When the old folks wanted to build a farmhouse, they would gather all the stones they could manage, and then ask all the neighbours to come to help. If they could have a house built in one day, with smoke coming out of the chimney by the evening and a fence of sorts around the smallholding, or *Tyddyn*, the house was theirs." John nodded emphatically, pleased to be able to expound his knowledge of local history.

"So, how did they manage that?" I asked, as he took another sip of his tea and relished the wide-eyed anticipation of his audience.

"Well, at dawn all the local families would turn up and set to with whatever they could do to help," he continued. "Passing the stones, packing the mud in between the stones, staking out the boundary; it did not need to be a fancy fence, just a rope or a wire strung between the piles of stones on each of the corners. They could come back to make the stone walls to separate the fields later, but the house being built and a good fire set blazing in the hearth was all that was necessary for that day."

My imagination was tantalized by that fascinating story of generous neighbourliness. I could picture the encouraging scene of a cloud of local families drifting up the lane over a hundred and forty years ago to come to help build what would become *Tŷ'n*

Llain. I envisioned the farmers' wives with their coarse woollen headscarves pulled tightly over their heads and their wooden clogs scraping across the stones. I imagined their long, flowing dresses and starched white aprons wafting in the morning breeze and wrapping themselves around the baskets of homemade food being carried in readiness to supply the army of workers for the day ahead. I could almost hear the squeals of delight from the children running excitedly before their parents over the dew-laden turf. I could see the farmers trudging up the lane in their worn clothing, brandishing rustic tools that gleamed in the soft pink light of dawn as it tinged the crest of Mynydd Mechell.

"So, what does this have to do with the toad in the wall, John?" Ever practical and objective, Philip broke into my daydream and abruptly returned me to the twentieth century. John flinched noticeably at this challenge to his centre stage and ran his hand down the back of his leathery neck, a habit we came to recognize as a sign that told us not to completely believe all he said.

"Well, maybe the toad got into the wall while it was being built and before the walls were plastered," he suggested.

"What would he have eaten?" Daniel asked

"Oh, there would have been plenty of insects and woodlice in the soil between the stones, Daniel," Philip replied. "But one hundred and forty years, John?"

"Well, you said it was a very big toad," John countered, deciding that his History lesson was over, and it was time to get back to something pressing at *Bryn Awel*. It was tempting to fully believe in John's motives and, as we came to know him better, we found him to be quite a likeable scoundrel.

John detested gorse, as it was the ideal hiding place for adders, which are very common in those hard, rocky parts of Anglesey and was why he found the old footpath between our homes too risky to navigate. One time that he did brave that route, he produced a yard-long snakeskin that had recently been discarded by its owner and was left draped over the stile. We could sometimes hear the snakes slithering over the stone walls around the fields, their scales quietly 'shushing' as they moved. From time to time the smell of burning gorse would waft across the valley and we knew it would be coming from somewhere around *Bryn Awel.*

On one visit, John offered Philip his Howard 500 rotovator.

"It is an excellent tool, Philip, ideal for any smallholder," John was selling his product with animated enthusiasm as the men sat together at the table outside the kitchen window on that unusually still day. "It has all kinds of attachments for cultivating the soil – potato ridging tool, harrows, single furrow plough and of course the usual rotary tines."

"Is it orange?" Philip asked, remembering the orange-coloured rotovator his father had owned many years earlier.

"Of course! Orange is the only colour for this kind of machine," John replied in his lilting Welsh accent.

"Hmmm…" Philip was certainly tempted. "How much do you want for it?" John's eyes hooded over as he leaned back on his seat and took a long draw on his tea. Casually brushing away some biscuit crumbs from the tablecloth, he considered the matter for a moment as though he had not given much thought to the price.

"No, no, Philip, you are a good friend…just a bottle of whisky will do," he replied, shaking his head emphatically. Philip delivered the whisky on Friday, saying he would return with his trailer to pick up the rotovator on Monday.

Early and eagerly on Monday morning he drove his vehicle, with the attached trailer he had recently purchased, into the muddy farmyard of *Bryn Awel.* John Owen was engrossed in repairing a log saw with his neighbour, John Henry, locally known as 'Jack', who was a short and stocky contrast to John Owen's tall, lean frame. The two Johns had been best friends forever and they only ever spoke in the Welsh language between them. Now in their late forties, they had grown up together in Mynydd Mechell, neither of them having ventured too far from their beloved *Ynys Môn*, the Welsh name for Anglesey.

John Henry was a quiet, gentle shepherd who wore a winter woollen coat, summer, winter, rain, or shine, which was usually secured with sisal baler twine. No one knew whether he had hair, for he always wore his cloth flat cap, indoors and out. He lived in a tiny tumbledown shepherd's batch called *Pant Glas*, which was close to the entrance to John Owen's house. It was a quaint little cottage, with typical whitewashed walls and the obligatory cement-covered Welsh slates on its low roof. Drab grey sacking hung against the two small windows to serve as curtains and, with its peeling blue paint, the only door to the house was so small that even John Henry had to duck to go through it. The batch nestled snugly into a cove in the rocks, where it was well protected from the strong westerly winds and was surrounded by four pretty stone-walled fields.

John Henry had an extraordinary way with animals; he would communicate gently with sheep, cattle, horses, his beloved cat, or John Owen's stock dogs. Every year, his cottage was home to many grateful orphan lambs and each night he was there to feed and comfort his young charges until they were independent and strong enough to move out into the fields with the other sheep.

Philip leapt enthusiastically from the microbus and scanned the farmyard for his anticipated rotovator. John Owen put down his tools and wiped his hands down the trousers of his blue boiler suit. John Henry, tools still in hand, straightened his back and watched as the two men walked across the yard towards each other. Both Johns knew why Philip had come that morning.

"Philip, Philip," wailed John Owen, beating his chest in feigned grief and theatrical protestations worthy of any Shakespearean

38

actor. "Someone has stolen your rotovator!" Something told Philip he had been tricked and that the rascal had double-sold his rotovator. So, yielding to the unchangeable, he asked for his whisky back.

"Oh, sorry, Philip, it's all gone!" John replied nonchalantly, returning to the project of repairing the log saw. John Henry gave Philip a grin and a wink, meaning 'you will be wiser next time!'

John Owen & John Henry 'Jack'

5 The Woolly Chess Board

"So, you are a landowner Mr......ah, Mr....Barlow?" The man representing the Ministry of Agriculture had invited Philip into his office in Llangefni and seemed quite interested in his case. "And how many acres do you own, Mr Barlow?" The man asked, with his pen poised over the large pad of blotting paper on his desk.

"We have fifteen acres now, Mr Evans," Philip replied proudly, leaning forward in his chair to ensure that Mr Evans was making careful notes on the paperwork bearing his name. Mr Evans blinked a few times but could not hide the condescending look that crossed his face. He was evidently used to dealing with large farm owners, not small-time hopefuls.

"What revenue did your farm bring you last year, Mr Barlow?" Mr Evans had a procedure to follow, which Philip could tell he was doing as politely as possible.

"We have only just bought the farm, and there are no fences," Philip explained.

"Ah, well no, sorry, we can only give grants to farmers who have already shown themselves to be making a good profit." Mr Evans put down his pen, leaned back in his chair and assumed a practised smile of benevolence.

"But how can I make a profit if I cannot put sheep on the land because there are no fences, Mr Evans?" Philip frowned and wondered about the logic of this policy.

"I do not make the rules, Mr Barlow, it is just my job to apply them," Mr Evans replied with a sigh and a slight shake of his head. Silence reigned in the office while Philip considered the possibility of another strategy. However, the fixed smile on the face of the man with the power of veto told him there was no use in kicking against the system.

"I don't suppose there is any point in my asking for a drainage grant then?" Philip proffered with a note of ill-disguised sarcasm. Mr Evans raised his eyebrows and looked meaningfully at Philip over his half-moon glasses. "No, I didn't think so," Philip said and took his leave.

'Llangefni is the County Town of Anglesey, and is also the centre of local government, enterprise and industry. Situated in the centre of Anglesey on the River Cefni, it has long held the market for livestock of all sorts and is a very important part of Anglesey's very long history.' So read the guide from the Tourist Information office.

It was mid-morning on a chilly December day when we arrived at Llangefni market, and the children were wide-eyed with excitement at all the sounds, smells and activity. After the calm and quiet of the farm, the bustle of the marketplace was another world. There were stalls of all kinds vying for our attention, some selling brightly-coloured local vegetables, others offering farm tools, kitchen utensils, or clothing. Joshua's big blue eyes peered hopefully over the rim of one of the tables at the gleaming array of penknives. Amelia was fascinated by the multi-coloured scarves that hung tantalizingly just beyond her reach from underneath the canopies. Daniel needed a hat to keep him warm against the wind and cold for when he helped his father around the farm, and I found some snug-looking woollen ones with an attractive, spiky leaf embroidered on the front, so I bought two.

However, we were there that day to get an idea of the cost and choices of sheep breeds, so we followed the strong smell of animals and found the cattle pens at the far end of the market. There, cows clattered noisily down the ramps from the transporter trucks and were herded into stout metal pens before being led individually into the straw-strewn arena.

Photo Credit~ Daily Post North Wales Live

It was a time for social gathering; the farmers, who had likely come from some distance, were relishing the event. Many wore tweed jackets and flat caps, with dark-coloured trousers tied in tightly with large leather belts. Some were dressed in boiler suits, tucked into rubber boots, while a few wealthy landowners could be identified by their smart jackets, ties and polished leather boots. We watched as the farmers warmly greeted one another like old friends. Many were relaxed and jovial, evidently enjoying this weekly diversion as a welcome break from working on the farm. Others looked quite anxious, perhaps wondering if they would get a good price if they were selling or, if they were buying, unsure of whether the prices were being pushed up by a collaborative team who were friends of the seller, not the buyer. They all seemed very genial until the auction started, and then suddenly it was every farmer for himself!

The auctioneer from Bob Parry's stood on the podium in his tan-coloured overall, with gavel in hand as a symbol of his uncontested right of office. He assessed the gathering of farmers seated on the wooden benches surrounding the auction ring before starting the bidding on the cattle. Although interesting, our attention was diverted to the sheep pens. It was fascinating to see all the shapes, sizes, colours and characteristics of the different breeds of sheep in their separate enclosures, waiting to be auctioned off. The smell of lanolin from the sheep's fleece filled the air and mingled with the succulent aroma of frying sausages, which wafted in from the hot dog stands in the marketplace.

"Hello, what are you doing here?" We had been so absorbed in the atmosphere that we had not noticed our friend, Ernie the plumber, come up behind us until he tapped Philip on the shoulder.

"Oh, hello, Ernie," Philip replied, pleased to see a familiar face. "Yes, we are thinking of buying some sheep for the land. And you?"

"I just like to come along on market day to see if there are any bargains," Ernie said with a rosy-cheeked smile as he greeted each of us cheerfully. "Watch out," he added with a wink and a nod, "these farmers are very shrewd; they know their worth!"

"Farmers need to be very discerning in balancing the purchase and other costs with the likely profit margin I can see," Philip commented sagely. "They will need to calculate the expected return on the finished animal ready for slaughter while taking into account the benefits of government subsidies, stock grants and allowances."

"I'm sure they do," Ernie and I agreed as we studied the manner of the bidders and the expressions on their faces. The auctioneer climbed up onto a running board that stretched the entire length of the sheep pens, rang a brass bell, and everyone obediently assembled around the first pen. At that moment, a great deal of commotion erupted in the cattle department, and everyone's attention turned in that direction. The disturbing sounds of shouts, shrieks and the scuffing of boots on the concrete floor were coming worryingly nearer as people ran in various directions. Then the crowd around the auctioneer rapidly dispersed as a large Welsh Black steer came thundering through the marketplace toward us! Philip, Ernie and I grabbed each of the three children and hurried them to safety. The terrified young steer was more bent on escape than menace, so the beast cavorted wildly around before charging out toward the market entrance, where the shouting and the crashing of overturned stalls marked his progress. Through the ensuing debris and pandemonium, the steer could be seen as a flash of black in the distance as it hurtled up the main street, with its owner and several other farmers in hot pursuit.

"Hey, what is this you have bought?" Ernie asked as he helped us soothe the children and pick up the remains of our purchases scattered across the floor. "So, you like marijuana, do you?" He suggested, grinning cheekily while holding up the woollen hats I had bought for Daniel. I took them from him and examined the design of the leaves embroidered on them.

"Are they marijuana leaves, Ernie?" I asked with some embarrassment.

"Yes, you wouldn't want to send young Daniel out wearing one of these," he warned.

"Ooh, thank you, Ernie," I said gratefully, looking sheepishly at Philip. "I will go back and swap them for something else, if the stall I bought them from still exists after the efforts of that runaway steer!" That was neither the first nor the last time we would be grateful for Ernie's wise advice.

With the panic over, everyone reassembled around the auctioneer as though such excitement was a regular marketplace occurrence. Climbing back onto his platform, he sounded his bell again, and the bidding began. The rapid speech that ensued was utterly incomprehensible for us who had not the least idea whether it was spoken in Welsh or English. The Welsh Mountain ewes were packed tightly into their pens; they were the more numerous at the market, like low-value 'pawns' on a chessboard amongst the motley gathering. Such a gentle breed with alert, warm brown eyes set in tan-coloured faces and ears coated in short, silvery-white fine hair. They wore abundant off-white fleece, sometimes displaying a collar of coarse red/brown hair amongst the wool and a thick, shaggy tail that reached almost to the ground.

In stark contrast, the Suffolk ewes were almost double the size and of much higher value than the Welsh Mountain sheep and stood regally as though conscious of their rank. Their fleece was a short, thick, firm and creamy crimp, like a dense eiderdown. Their ears, lower legs and faces were the colour of the darkest chocolate, and they had immodestly short-docked tails. They were frequently only six to a pen and their superior air likened them to the 'Queen' in this game of chess.

The 'Welsh Mules' were crossbred to produce a larger ewe, but with the hardiness of the Welsh Mountain sheep. One example was the Border Leicester cross, which had inherited from their fathers, funny, bunny rabbit ears and an aquiline nose. Not a pretty animal, but very useful; the 'Rooks' in the chess game, one might say. Each time the auctioneer tapped his clipboard with the butt of his pencil to indicate, 'Sold', our three children clung tightly to our sides as we were jostled along to the next pen. Eventually, we moved with the crowd to the stadium, where the rams were displayed one at a time. Only the well-informed were aware of the identity of the first ram for sale, a tall, stately-looking animal that strolled proudly into the arena. He was a local breed, so someone kindly explained to us; not well known elsewhere. Looking somewhat like a llama, with the shaggy fleece of the Welsh Mountain sheep and a relatively small, black spotted head atop its long white neck, the Beulah ram stood head and shoulders above all the rest; well suited as the chessboard 'Bishop'.

"Sold!" declared the auctioneer, after rapid bidding, and then the next ram was led in for display. With silvery-white short hair on their entire head and legs and a dense white fleece covering oversized buttocks, the Texel rams were fetching outrageous amounts of money; obviously, a meat variety for producing first-rate, fat lambs. This breed of ram, we concluded, vied with the stocky Suffolk ram for the position of 'King' of our imaginary chessboard.

Daniel, Amelia and Joshua were enthralled by the experience; however, they were beginning to tire of watching sheep, so we led them to the pens of piglets and puppies, which did appeal to them. Their little faces beamed with delight as they were permitted to cuddle the puppies, and each had a favourite.

"What would Poppy think if we took home another puppy?" Philip tried to reason with them as their big blue eyes all turned towards us hopefully. The smell of frying sausages was becoming increasingly tempting as we approached lunchtime, which distracted them from further pleading, so we hurried through the rest of the market to the hot dog stand. Despite having enjoyed a well-spent morning, it was evident that there was so much to consider before buying sheep. Moreover, we decided that Llangefni market was probably not the place to buy or sell unless we were astute locals or seasoned regulars.

6 Mr Cledwyn Davies

It was already becoming dark by four o'clock a few evenings later when we heard the crunch of tyres on the driveway. As visitors were infrequent, everyone rushed to the window and peered into the shadows while the vehicle turned and parked. A lean black-and-white dog, like a cross between a Collie and a Greyhound, paced up and down in the canvas-covered back of the vehicle. However, we did not recognize the man who emerged from the white Peugeot pick-up truck, wearing the typical flat cap and tweed jacket. The man strolled amiably and confidently toward Philip, who had gone outside to greet him, and introduced himself as Mr Davies from Bethesda in the Snowdonia Mountains.

"Prynhawn Da," Philip replied as the men shook hands. He was pleased to have the chance to practice the Welsh greeting he had been learning and invited Mr Davies into the kitchen. Explaining the reason for his visit, Mr Davies said he had heard from his fencer, John Owen that we might be interested in a reasonably priced flock of sheep that he had to sell. They were what he called 'broken mouth ewes', which were older sheep or those missing a few teeth and were finding difficulty grazing the sparse herbage of the mountains of Snowdonia.

"They should be good for a few more years at your lower altitude with its 'softer climate,'" he assured us, suggesting we visit his farm to view them. Philip and his helpful young assistants had not quite finished all the fencing around the lower fields, and the top fields had no fences at all, the boundaries being marked only by ancient stone walls. Nevertheless, the following Friday, we had a family outing to Snowdonia, finishing the day by visiting Mr Davies on his farm at Rachub, on the Carneddau Range overlooking Bethesda.

The black-and-white Collie we had noticed in the back of the pick-up truck when Mr Davies came to visit us, bounded around, barking to announce our arrival as we drove into the concrete farmyard. Mr Davies was in one of the sheep pens, ankle-deep in 'aromatic' sheep daggings, or tousled and matted clumps of wool and dung, cut from around their tails and back legs.

"Just the last few to do," Mr Davies called out as he reached for the lanyard attached to an old red Lister shearing machine, which chattered into life. Leaning over the metal railings, we all watched in fascination as he swung the whirring hand piece skilfully around the back-end of the sheep wedged between his knees. Soon he pushed the last well-groomed sheep through a little door at the side of the pen, where she skipped off, clean and joyous, to join the rest of the flock. Mr Davies stood up stiffly, stretching his aching back. Wiping his hands on his trousers and kicking aside the piles of daggings, he reached out to shake Philip's hand. I gave him a gracious wave and stood back in case he offered his hand to me too.

"I have put the sheep over here, ready for you to look at," he said, greeting the children cheerily before leading the way. There were about a hundred Welsh Mountain sheep in the pens, each with two cuts in one of their ears, which we learned was Mr Davies' mark to identify his own when they came down from communal grazing on the mountains. Philip noted that the sheep had unusual tan faces with minimal spotting.

"Yes," Mr Davies replied, "I have been breeding this strain for many years, and they are quite distinct." What was more noticeable was the patch of thick red wax on the backs of their heads.

"Is that another one of your identifying marks Mr Davies?" Philip asked naïvely.

"Call me, Cledwyn," Mr Davies replied. "No, these sheep are not for eating; they are only for breeding," he explained. "When the nuclear accident happened in Chernobyl last year, this region was covered in radioactive rain; the sheep absorbed a lot of it, so now only the lambs can be used for human consumption."

Of course, Chernobyl! We were well aware of the tragic accident at the nuclear power station. The fallout from that terrible disaster had reportedly affected a far greater area than its immediate surroundings in Ukraine. However, we had not considered the lasting effects on this North-western region of the British Isles. The toxic cloud of destruction that emanated from the nuclear power station had wafted menacingly northward from its origin, settling itself in all its ugly 'glory' upon the Northern reaches of Europe! Whether we were truly unaffected in the South of England, or if we were persuaded to believe that, we did not know; however, Mr Davies' information certainly gave us something to consider.

Heading back towards the farmhouse to discuss the number and price of the sheep we were to purchase, the children noticed a dirty, bedraggled sheepdog tied up inside one of the barns.

"She is too timid for me to use," Mr Davies explained with irritation in his voice. "No use for rounding up the sheep on the mountains; I need a strong dog like my Tweed here," he said with a warm smile as he patted the head of his close companion affectionately. Tweed, who knew he was loved and appreciated, responded by bounding in a happy, tail-wagging circle around his master.

The following morning, while we were still finishing breakfast, Mr Davies arrived in his stock wagon, carrying our new flock of sheep. Tweed leapt from the front cab of the vehicle, and stood in a half-crouched poise, ready to discipline and steer them in the right direction. Several sheep skipped delightedly on being released from their uncomfortable prison as they poured out from the back of the wagon and funnelled into the field overlooking *Llyn Bwch*. Mr Davies then drew our attention to a woven Hazelwood sheep hurdle in the shadowy depths of the vehicle, which restrained three more sheep.

"Seventy-five ewes and one for luck," he beamed as he proudly led out a nervous-looking ewe and explained it was the custom to throw in an extra animal for goodwill, just in case one of them should die. Mr Davies pulled at the twisted jaw of the ewe to demonstrate that she still had some teeth, but her mouth was broken when she was young. We decided to call her Jemimah, and she turned out to be one of our best sheep.

From the depths of the truck, a majestic sight in the form of a proud and personable Welsh Mountain ram emerged. His shaggy white coat reached almost to the ground and his enormous, spiralled horns wrapped around his ears, framing his face. Although he was not a tall sheep, he had the presence of nobility as he lifted his proud, arched Roman nose to survey his new kingdom; Philip decided to call him Nero. Nero was followed by the final addition to our new flock, one of the 'Bishops' such as we had seen in Llangefni market. Tall, stately and hornless, with a black and white spotted face, this Beulah ram walked with unhurried dignity down the ramp of the truck and stood quietly beside his woolly companion. Philip decided he should be known as Augustus or Gus for short, and the two rams seemed like good friends rather than competitors for the flock.

"One ram for every forty or fifty ewes," Mr Davies informed us to explain the need for two rams. Philip counted out the cash agreed upon and passed it gratefully into his hands, but Mr Davies looked hurt and disappointed, and Philip was puzzled.

"Was this not what we agreed upon, Mr Davies?" he asked.

"Yes," replied Mr Davies. "But an extra one for luck is the tradition."

"Oh, yes, of course!" Philip quickly pressed another pound coin into Mr Davies' hand, and the shepherd's kindly, weather-reddened face broke into a satisfied smile. Philip was sure it was not because he needed the money but because, like many country people, he liked to keep the old traditions alive. It was another lesson learned.

Saffron **Beulah Ram**   **Welsh Mountain Ram**

Although we considered the Welsh Mountain sheep to be underrated, Mr Davies had undoubtedly chosen the best of the sheep we had seen in his pen at Bethesda the day before. While he seemed well pleased that they had gone to a good home, we felt we had a flock of which we could be proud. With a warm, friendly handshake and a pat on the back, the deal was done.

Mr Davies wanted to take one last look at the flock and demonstrate the skills of his sheepdog. Daniel, Amelia and Joshua climbed onto the solid wooden field gate Philip had made, so they could watch as Tweed dashed energetically into the field. Responding to the shrill whistles and waves from his master, he quickly rounded up all the sheep into a compliant group. Mr

Davies beamed with pride, watching the impression his well-trained sheepdog had on we novices. We all leaned on the gate, looking across our new flock, drinking tea with Mr Davies and watching the waters of *Llyn Bwch* (Lake of the mountain pass) glistening in the morning sunlight. It was the perfect ending to a pleasant morning. We felt we had found a trustworthy, well-meaning associate in Mr Cledwyn Davies, which time would prove to be the case.

One late afternoon a few days later, we were again leaning on the farm gate, watching the sheep grazing contentedly. On the horizon behind Mynydd Y Garn, the sun was settling down onto a pastel pink and yellow gauze that tinged the gorse-strewn hills with its glow. A wispy mist had started to unfurl from the lake and was wafting mystically upward like delicate treble clefs and musical notes. We bathed in that magical experience in total wonder, not wanting to move for fear of missing a moment of that transfixing vision as it blended decoratively with the fresh evening air.

We then became aware of the incoming presence of a flock of white swans. We could hear them before we could see them; a formation of about a dozen of them was heading toward the lake, honking loudly with their black legs tucked up tidily behind them. Then, with the poise of a ballet troupe, they swirled in unison over the lake and began their descent in a perfect, fascinating wide spiral. The delicate, hazy patterns over the water dispersed, and the misty notes, crotchets and semi-quavers swirled into elegant vortexes as the swans' wings cut through the vapour and the birds glided gracefully to rest on the lake.

"Whooper Swans!" Arthur from *Pencae* confirmed when he came to see our new flock. "From Iceland, so they say. Come to these parts at about this time every year they do, and leave in the spring." We had first noticed them about a month earlier. Still, we were pleased to have Arthur's confirmation since those lovely birds with their black and yellow beaks and long thin necks held erect were not visitors to those regions of Southern England where we had lived. Every morning at sunrise, they would rise from the lake with their strong wings slapping the surface of the water noisily, and with a lot of hooting and honking, they would head for *Llyn Alaw*, a large lake to the southeast of us. There they would spend the day feeding on the prolific weed and then return every evening to roost on *Llyn Bwch*, where a thick, impenetrable fortress of Norfolk reeds surrounding the lake protected them from almost every sort of predator. It was another delight to add to our growing list of discoveries.

7 Athaliah the Rebel Sheep

For many years a photo hung on the wall of my parent's home of their four daughters at the wedding of my sister Diane and her husband, Michael. Diane looked exquisite in the cream satin medieval style wedding dress, which had been worn by our mother more than thirty years earlier, while we three sisters were dressed rather theatrically to match the style. I was wearing a grey felt riding hat that I had found in a little shop in Boston, Lincolnshire. It had a white veil, topped with a plume of white feathers, which was complemented by a dark blue velvet cape.

What was particularly appealing about the photo was that it caught us all in the middle of hoots of laughter at Kim, the cameraman. In his effort to capture that precious moment, he had forgotten that he was holding a pint of beer and had promptly tipped the entire contents of the glass down his immaculate suit! Kim had since been a long-time friend and a frequent source of accidental amusement. So we were pleased to hear that he and his lovely wife, Dean, had come to stay with Paul and Candy over the winter holidays and they asked if they could bring their baby daughter, April, to come to visit us on our farm.

It was a crisp, bright, but chilly day when the two families bundled excitedly in through the kitchen door. Kim was the same as ever with a cheeky smile on his face, framed by his dark, curly hair. In his familiar style of a black leather jacket over blue jeans, he managed the old casual charm we remembered so well. Dean, a picture of petite and quiet dignity, glided into the room, her hair and makeup flawless despite the ravages of our windy climate. I found myself nervously polishing the enamel kettle that was singing comfortably on the stove and brushing cornflakes off kitchen chairs for them to sit down on. Cradling her well-wrapped baby, Dean gazed with interest around the room. It was apparent that she had not ventured into a farmhouse before and, as I offered to relieve her of her black leather jacket, I uttered a silent prayer of thanks that the gaping and embarrassing hole in the kitchen wall had been repaired. Dean looked as though she was contemplating politely removing her stilettos, as people from the South of England are accustomed to doing until she spotted the diagonal green trail that travelled across the kitchen carpet from the back door to the door leading to the bathroom.

"Carpet in the kitchen?" my mother had exclaimed when she heard what the sales representative had persuaded me to buy. "You will rue the day you decided upon that!" she had warned.

However, by the time I had called the sales representative back at the shop, he was sorry to say that the carpet had already been cut and was ready to lay. So, rue the day we did, particularly since we discovered that, in general, Northerners were less inclined to remove their shoes when coming to visit, even after traipsing across our land with Philip. Hence, the green trail of sheep deposits was a constant source of irritation and hard work to keep scrubbed and clean.

The buzz of noisy chatter around the kitchen table indicated that the visitors were enjoying some 'catch-up' time and the men had given up on the idea of tea and had already broken into the stash of beer they had brought with them. The children were just on the point of taking Natasha and Hadleigh up to their bedrooms to play with their toys, when suddenly Philip, who was passing the kitchen window, let out a shout of annoyance:

"That wretched sheep! She has gotten into the top fields again!" Everyone in the room was shocked by the outburst and wondered what had happened. Sleeping baby April awoke at the noisy eruption and started to cry. "I just can't keep her in, no matter what I do," Philip explained to the bemused group as he donned his wax jacket and tweed hat and threw open the back door. We had been well pleased with all the sheep that Mr Davies had sold us, except for this one rebel. She respected no boundaries, she could scale any fence and there she was, defiantly, on the wrong side of the fence, calling to the rest of the flock to follow her. Philip hated that sheep for defeating him at every turn and decided to name her 'Athaliah' after an infamous Biblical queen.

"Anyone coming to help me get her back in?" he called over his shoulder, as he tugged on his rubber boots. There was a sudden scramble of volunteers, who started pulling on coats, hats and boots, and followed Philip up to the top fields. By the time we adults arrived on the scene, Philip had already enlisted the help of the children, who found the excitement of running around chasing Athaliah sheep to be highly amusing. Even Jeffrey horse had trotted across to the corner of his paddock to investigate and was whinnying and skipping about friskily. However, Philip was getting very frustrated and increasingly irritated by the stubborn refusal of his antagonist to comply with his efforts to drive her back to home ground.

Kim, who had strolled up at a leisurely pace to join the excitable crowd, was still clutching his pint of beer and seemed to be finding the whole event very entertaining.

"Open the gate! Open the gate!" Philip called urgently to anyone who was nearest, as the sheep was finally driven in the right direction. Paul made a lunge for the latch on the long wooden gate but Athaliah did not wait for it to swing open. She took a running leap over the wire-topped stone wall and, unfortunately for Kim, landed on his leather-clad shoulder! She then bounded off back to join the rest of her flock, with Philip running behind her, hurling irritated threats in her direction. Yet again, Kim was covered in beer and Candy and I were in hoots of laughter at him. Some things never change.

With the crisis over, our visitors returned to the warmth of the kitchen, where Dean was soothing baby April back to sleep while watching the charade from the kitchen window. Everyone was ready for lunch and beer glasses were replenished, while Kim dried himself as best as possible by the warmth from the Rayburn, from which issued the inviting aroma of a hearty casserole.

The children chattered happily in the corner of the kitchen, Amelia and Natasha playing with their dolls, Daniel, Hadleigh and Joshua with their little motor cars, the men reminiscing over old times and the Mums talking about babies. Only I seemed to take any notice of the growing green trail across the kitchen floor; 'but forget it,' I decided; 'that will be tomorrow's job.'

Philip's battle with Athaliah sheep was by no means over. He continued diligently constructing the fencing away into the distance of the top fields and every so often, a blurred green form would speed across the horizon in pursuit of the errant Athaliah sheep. Then it was action stations again, with everyone on alert to run to help with the chase.

8 Anglesey Road Protocol

Thanks to our conversations with our neighbours, Dewi, the *postmon*, Llew Jones the coalman, and the patient indulgence of the postmistress in Llanfechell post office, by January, we were beginning to form a few words and phrases in Welsh. One of our English friends who came to visit informed us that she was becoming quite proficient in Welsh, just through reading the road signs. She could now say with confidence: "Hello. How are you? Beware of side winds!"

We had also noticed that there were attractive pieces of poetry dotted along many of the country roads, which we learned by heart, such as *Pan welwch olau coch, sefwch yma* or in English: When red light shows wait here.

It soon became apparent that making friends on Anglesey would be quite a painless affair, likely because our children were three lovable extroverts (according to their Granny). In general, we found the Welsh people to be particularly kind to children; what was more, being new neighbours from the 'faraway South of England', we seemed to be a subject for much curiosity.

Most of the local populace was interrelated, so everyone behaved pleasantly to each other, just in case. We quickly learned that we needed one hand for driving and the other for waving, which was a very genial custom but could sometimes prove to be a rather dangerous and tricky business. The main road down to the village was in some places only a single track, edged with unforgiving stone walls, which skirted every old and cherished tree and respected every long-held boundary. Therefore, it was preferable to keep both hands on the steering wheel.

Once I found myself in a situation that I was sure would end in a collision, being sandwiched between an impatient motorcyclist behind and a tractor ahead, which was coming towards us at a remarkable speed! There was nothing I could do except to grip the steering wheel, close my eyes and hope for the best.

"It's all right, Mum, you can go on now," Daniel said, as he poked

me in the side, and when I looked up, the tractor had passed us and the motorcycle was speeding along the narrow, twisting road ahead.

"What happened?" I asked, surprised that there had been no incident. "I had my eyes closed."

"Yes, so did the man driving the tractor," Daniel assured me.

It seemed to be generally accepted that any unfortunate altercation would be handled politely as 'knock for knock'. I overheard this conversation between two local ladies while I was waiting in the queue in Llanfechell Post Office one morning:

"Oh dear, I don't know what my John will say when he sees that awful dent in the front of the car; he has only just had it resprayed; he will be hopping mad. There was no way I could have avoided

Will Owen; he was driving that taxi so fast!"

"But you will be able to claim on his insurance, surely?" I suggested innocently, trying to be encouraging. Both ladies involved in the conversation turned horrified stares in my direction.

"Dear me, no; I could not possibly do that," the first lady stated firmly. "Will Owen is my husband's Auntie's brother-in-law!"

On another occasion, while passing the local school, I witnessed an elderly lady reverse her car into the side of the vehicle parked on the opposite side of the road. Stopping the car, I watched as the lady drove forward slightly, got out of her car, gave a cursory examination of the damage, then climbed back into her car and drove off gracefully down the road. Just then, the owner of the damaged vehicle returned and gave an understandable utterance of dismay, watching helplessly as the offender disappeared into the distance.

"Don't worry!" I called out heroically as I ran toward her, waving a slip of paper on which I had hastily written. "I have her registration number here."

"What?" she exclaimed aghast, "I would not dream of doing anything about it. That is old Nurse Hughes, the local midwife; she delivered me, my sisters, my mother, my aunties and my uncles!" I screwed up my offending piece of paper and considered that I had learned another valuable lesson.

Little black-headed Suffolk lambs began to appear in the fields during the wet, cold days of January. Clinging tightly to their mothers' sides to shelter from the biting winds, the poor little creatures had been thrust into the cruel realities of winter weather. Early lambs, being first on the supermarket shelves, brought a higher price, but it was a tough time for the sheep and their shepherds.

To lighten one grey, dreary January day, I invited my friend Sandra and her children Jason, Kirsty and Charlotte to come with us to the beach at Cemlyn Head after they had finished school. Although having fallen heavily for several days, the rain had eased a bit, so it was a treat for our children to leave the farm to meet up with their friends. Unfortunately, it had not occurred to me when I parked our Volkswagen Microbus on the grass verge leading to the beach that it would have become as soggy as a sponge. Everyone leapt from the bus excitedly, only to find themselves ankle-deep in mud. What was worse, the wheels of the bus started to sink slowly into the mire.

"Oh, no!" Sandra commiserated. "What can we do to help?" Looking around for inspiration, I noticed that the track leading to the beach was covered in smooth, round stones, so I suggested we gather them and throw them into the sodden verge in front of the bus wheels. It was a game that the children played with enthusiasm until they decided they had done enough, and the lure of the beach distracted them.

"Do you want to go ahead and take them down to the beach, Sandra?" I suggested. "I think we should be all right now." I was also worried that the unavoidable wheel spinning would kick up a lot of mud, which it certainly did. The bus heaved and whined as the tires spun and skidded on the spot sending mud spraying high into the air as the vehicle sank deeper into the troughs it had chewed into the grass verge. More stones thrown behind the wheels did not work, and neither did a long plank of wood that I found discarded in the ditch. The light was starting to dwindle, and I knew if I did not find some way to extricate my vehicle very soon, it would be stuck there for the night.

I had hoped my training as the daughter of a second-hand car dealer would put me in good stead. My sisters and I enjoyed working for my father, and there were rarely dull moments. He taught us how to extricate ourselves from difficult situations when driving some of the antiquated motors he had taken in part exchange for a more modern vehicle.

"Just take this car out, drive it around for a while and tell me what is wrong with it," Dad would say. He taught us how to reinstall a starter motor that would drop out and need replacing every time we stopped the car. We learned how to 'double-declutch' when the synchromesh was worn out on the gears and that a good hammer was an essential tool for firming down battery terminals that had come loose. We cleaned the cars and the engines, learned how to change a tyre and identify the causes of strange knocking, ticking, or grinding sounds. My sister, Terrie, knew how to remove the sump plug to change the oil on the vehicles, and one time a sales representative came into the office and, with due concern, exclaimed:

"Hey, George, your mechanic is under a car out there, and he has painted toenails!"

"I found out what is wrong with that Humber, Dad," I reported one day as I brandished the gear stick that had fallen out. It had not been easy to drive the six or more miles back to the garage in second gear! I discovered that doing a 'hill start' in a car with no working handbrake can cause uncomfortable distortions of the feet. Moreover, it was alarming when driving uphill, only to find oneself sliding backwards because the catch, which should have held the driver's seat in place, had been broken. Terrie appeared at the door to Dad's office one day with a steering wheel tucked under her arm with the explanation:

"It came off in my hands, Dad!"

While driving in the countryside one Sunday morning with my three sisters, I accidentally knocked off the exhaust pipe bracket on my Ford Anglia due to running over an exposed tree root. We were in the middle of nowhere, so we had to be resourceful; a pair of tights wrapped around the end of the exhaust pipe and protected by a leather glove at least got us home. Unfortunately, we forgot to tell Dad about the exhaust pipe when Mum plied us with the regular mountain of Sunday dinner. Even worse, we forgot to tell him about the problem before speeding up to Streatham, near London, to meet up with our friends at the ice rink that evening.

It was not until we were cruising home at seventy miles an hour on the outside lane of the A2 that we even remembered the delicate circumstance of our poor old exhaust pipe. A sudden BANG! interrupted our excited chatter and 'homeward bound' singing. Then colourful sparks, like fireworks, issued from behind the car when the rear end of the exhaust pipe dropped onto the road. It bounced noisily and dramatically as it was dragged across the tarmac in the wake of our vehicle, which I manoeuvred as swiftly as possible to the hard shoulder. Someone else had to sacrifice their tights, we unearthed another leather glove from the depths of the glove box, and then we were away again. We thought it was time to tell Dad about the exhaust pipe when we arrived home that night.

Something else Dad had taught us, however, was when to give up and ask for help. So now, with the microbus inextricably established in the massacred grass verge, my passengers all wanting to go home for their dinner and the cold evening air

wrapping itself around my defeated form, I decided it was time to take his advice.

Lights were beginning to appear in the windows of an old farmhouse, set back from the road; I had considered asking for help earlier in my dilemma but had seen no sign of life there. It was encouraging to see a pair of size 10 rubber boots at the back door of the farmhouse when I approached and knocked loudly to ensure that the occupants would hear me over the sound of the radio singing joyfully within. To my relief, the door swung open, and I found myself bathed in warmth and light from the kitchen, while the tempting aroma of cooking smells encircled and enticed me so it was hard to remain on the outside of the door. Thankfully, the face on the farmer's wife creased into a welcoming smile as she wiped her hands on her chequered apron and peered into the darkening shadows, where I stood, hopeful of a good response.

"Come in, come in!" the dear lady invited after hearing the garbled explanation of my plight, swinging the door fully open to reveal a kitchen oozing welcome.

"Sit down, sit down, Dear; you look like you could do with a nice cup of tea." I could tell there was no point in refusing as the lady pulled back a wooden chair, festooned with pretty, floral cushions, on which I was encouraged to sit. Almost instantly, she placed a steaming cup of tea before me on the red and white gingham tablecloth covering the long wooden table.

"He will be here in just a minute," the farmer's wife assured me, sitting down at the other end of the table with a bowl of carrots, which she started to peel in preparation for the evening meal. I sipped at my tea thankfully and attempted to make polite conversation. A tabby cat slumbered contentedly on the well-cushioned wooden settle flanking the wall-side of the table, oblivious of or disinterested in my presence. Through the lace-embellished low window, I could see the light was growing dimmer; I was feeling anxious for Sandra and the children, who I had left sitting in the bus, but there was nothing to be done until the farmer came in. The radio heralded the five o'clock news, and at that precise moment, the farmer emerged from a door at the far end of the kitchen and started to wash his hands at the kitchen sink.

"Ah, here he is!" his wife exclaimed with a blend of relief and reverence. "This lady needs some help, Dear," she explained in her charming Welsh accent, as she nodded and smiled at me. "She seems to have gotten her motor stuck in the mud." The farmer did not turn to acknowledge me but continued to wash his hands.

"Yes, I know," he replied over his shoulder. "She has been out there for over an hour now."

'WHAT!' My jaw dropped, and I stared open-mouthed at the back of the man; my thoughts raced, and my quick temper roused. 'You left me struggling for over an hour without coming to help me! I thought country people were kind, considerate and chivalrous! How could you have done this, knowing that I needed your help and I have children waiting in the bus who need to get home for their dinner?' I was so shocked that I said absolutely nothing but kept my indignant words right where they belonged.....Unspoken!

The farmer's wife, reading my expression, wisely apprehended any embarrassing outburst by kindly and soothingly explaining that her husband had just been dealing with a difficult lambing in the barn. On hearing this, I instantly regained control of my emotions and melted in wonderment.

"Twins!" the farmer announced jubilantly when he finally finished scrubbing at his forearms and turned around to face us. "So, stuck in the mud then," he stated unceremoniously, rubbing a towel over his arms and peering at me through the diffusion of steam issuing from the pot of carrots that his wife had set boiling on the stove. "We had better get out the tractor then."

Philip was relieved to see us when we finally returned home that evening, tired, hungry and covered in mud. Even though in this case the situation was caused by the poor judgment of the driver, in the short while we had owned the microbus, it had been rare for us not to return home in it without assistance. Therefore, we decided it was time to investigate a change of family vehicle, which we hoped would be better suited to the rigours of country life demanded of it.

9 The Tractor

Trees were a scarcity rather than a frequent sight in our part of the Island. Along with goat willows and downy birch in the boggy hollows, we treasured our line of sycamore trees that sheltered at least part of the lane leading to the world beyond. Other than that, a few scant hawthorns managed to survive at intervals along the rocky terrain. Bent over like ageing crofters with their backs to the wind, their presence told of the harsh, relentless gales they had survived. Philip said it was less a case of being bent over and more due to the tips of the branches being nipped off on their windward side. Either way, we were pleased there were at least some trees to be seen.

"Eggs and bacon," Philip had introduced me to the delights of nibbling on the tender young leaves of the hawthorn as they first appeared in the late spring when we lived in the south of England.

"Eggs and bacon?" I had queried, watching suspiciously to see what would happen to him as he relished this specimen of country delicacies.

"That's what we used to call them when I was a boy; try them," he suggested as he nipped off more of those young green buds and handed one to me. So many little things like that made me aware that this man was at one with Nature and I realised how much I had to learn from his ever-enquiring resourcefulness.

"You know, there should be more trees around here, it would certainly give us more shelter," he commented one morning as I was hanging the washing on the line." His eyes scanned our acreage from under his tweed fedora hat, while the wind slapped his face with the collar of his coat and I guessed we were about to embark on a new project.

"There! Easy!" Philip's powerful arms thrust the spade into the turf, quickly following with a deft stamp of his size 11 rubber boots to drive it deep into the hard and rocky soil. Another three such manoeuvres to form a square and, with expertise, a large clod of earth was removed to make way for the first of our tree plantation.

"Very good, Philip!" I commended him encouragingly, hoping that he might continue to demonstrate how to plant all the rest of the seedling trees he had set aside as my share of the planting project. Taking several long steps to demonstrate the number of paces to be taken to find the correct location for the next tree, he performed another smooth and perfect dissection to make sure I got the point of the lesson. Daniel and Amelia observed their father with open admiration, while Joshua was watching Poppy. She was not interested in planting trees but had found some fresh molehills, into which she was digging furiously, plunging her long nose into the holes that she uncovered.

"Will you be alright with that?" Philip was disinterested in hearing my answer I could tell, as he thrust the spade like a spear into the ground and perused the fence line I was supposed to follow. "I have shown you what to do, now please make sure you dig deep; these trees will need to withstand a tough adversary with the weather, so they will need to have a good and secure start."

Protestations, such as the fact that it was freezing cold, the ground was solid as ice and that I had a lot to do in the house, did not manage to make 'headlines' that day!

"You only have twenty to plant, you can manage them all before lunch, I know," Philip reassured me as he gripped the handles of the wheelbarrow, which was loaded with another fifty young trees, and set off in the direction of the next fence line. Daniel always loved to work beside his father and ran happily alongside him in his brown anorak and green rubber boots, his chestnut curls bouncing around his cherubic, smiling face.

I stood watching them until they disappeared beyond the stone wall separating the top and the lower fields, then I turned to observe my little team of workers. Poppy was still quite occupied with her molehill mining and must have been on the trail of the culprit, for she was now digging frantically and barking excitedly. Joshua, in his blue zip-up coat, ran over to investigate, so it looked as though it was just Amelia and me on my team. Although I guessed she would have preferred to have accompanied her Daddy, his fifty trees sounded like a lot of hard work and she was my ever-loyal little companion. Her long blond hair wafted wispily around her sweet little face from underneath her white woollen bonnet, while her blue eyes squinted against the morning brightness to see what I was going to do next.

"Let's get going then, Amelia," I said, struggling to pull the spade from the ground and walking the obligatory paces to the location of our first planting. Not surprisingly, my hole-digging rendered a smack of pathos compared to the expertise of her father but she stuck quietly beside me in anticipation of improvement, her white-mittened hand still holding onto the sapling she had chosen from the pile we had been assigned to plant. After several attempts at cutting a hole of suitable depth into that rocky terrain, I was beginning to feel defeated. It was just then that I had a bit of inspiration...

"Poppy! Poppy! What's this?" I called out, attempting to draw the attention of the little dog toward my efforts. Both she and Joshua ran over to see what was of interest.

"What is it, Poppy? What is it?" I repeated, hoping to drum up some enthusiasm for my cause. Poppy decided that I must have discovered the best of molehills and began to dig excitedly into the spot to which I was pointing. I took up my spade again to finish off the task after a few moments of Poppy's efficient excavation, and then Amelia was able to drop in the tree she had been dutifully holding for so long. I filled the hole with the previously evicted soil and we moved the necessary paces to the next planting position.

"You finished that quickly!" Philip was pleasantly surprised to  find us back in the kitchen, sitting drinking a nice *panad* and with a pot of soup boiling on the Rayburn's hotplate. "How did it go?" he asked as he and Daniel stripped off their coats, hung them on the back of the kitchen door and strode over to the sink to wash their hands.

"No problem really, was it, Amelia?" I replied as we smiled a cheeky smile at each other over our teacups, pleased that our assignment was successful and we could get back to less exertive and more essential things. "How about you?" I asked while pouring two cups of tea for our hard-working big men.

"We did really well, didn't we, Daniel? Got them all planted," Philip replied as he dried his hands on a towel and sat down to his cup of tea. Daniel, flushed with the morning's exertion, the wind battering or the sheer satisfaction of being his father's helper, joined us at the table with enthusiasm for his tea and biscuits. Philip's gaze began to wander through the window facing the lower fields, his second cup of tea held in contemplative suspense.

"You know, we could make something of that boggy acre in the lower fields," he said and I could see another arduous plan already forming in his head. "It is too wet and marshy for the sheep to run on, but it would make an ideal little copse. Yes, we will get some alder and willow trees and we can plant them before the spring arrives." I grimaced at Amelia, who judged it prudent to take another sip from her teacup.

Lunchtime was an animated affair, with chatter about trees and moles and helpful dogs; however, we became aware of the melodious sound of a machine approaching. We all rushed to the window to see a well-seasoned tractor in red and grey livery, which parked on the front driveway. The tinkling chime of a small hinged metal cap that flapped up and down with each puff of the vertical exhaust pipe at the front of the tractor, accompanied the burbling rhythm of the engine as it idled. This vision of harmony was starkly interrupted by a bright yellow attachment fixed to the back of the tractor, sticking out at an awkward angle like a gigantic grasshopper's leg.

We instantly recognised the driver in the blue boiler suit, as he jumped down from his seat and approached the house. John Owen wore a wide and congenial smile on his work-weary face as he accepted the offer of a *panad* with Philip, while the children and I finished our meal. Sitting together on the low brick wall surrounding the front of the house with the tractor still pulsating musically, John explained the reason for his unexpected visit.

"I have decided to buy a new tractor, Philip; I have a lot more fencing work to do, so I need to get a bigger tractor to be able to carry that post hammer on the back there."

"Ah," Philip replied, "I was wondering what that contraption was," he said, pointing to the yellow 'grasshopper leg' protruding from the back of the tractor. "So, this tractor is not strong enough?" he asked innocently.

"Oh, it's a good little tractor, Philip!" John countered and proceeded to extol the virtues of his long-term, trusty servant. Here before Philip was a Massey Ferguson 35, in 'original' condition and available for sale. Apparently, this was the very make and model of the tractor that Ed Hillary drove all the way to the South Pole, so John enlightened him. The old tractor continued to burble contentedly on the driveway, its blackened exhaust pipe quivering and sending up regular puffs of invisible gas to activate its tuneful cap. Philip had learnt about Edmund Hillary, the first man to climb to the summit of Mount Everest, but it was news to him that the same courageous man's expedition to the South Pole had been made on one of these little tractors.

"You will need to cut a crop of hay later in the year, Philip, and this tractor has a PTO, [Power Take Off], with a nice little mower that fits onto this here. It also has a two-furrow plough," John persisted, pointing at a slowly spinning shaft, mounted on its rear axle. Philip needed a few moments to take in this new idea presented to him; a bit of mechanical help around the farm was certainly something he could do with, he conceded.

"Hmmm..." Philip rather fancied himself as a ploughman, imagining being on the Canadian prairies, ploughing long straight furrows with the plough mouldboards gleaming as it turned the rich brown soil.

"I am not asking a great deal for it," John interrupted Philip's musings, proposing a very reasonable price. Having finished my meal, I joined the two men sitting on the wall. I could almost see the cogs whirring in Philip's brain as he thought over all that John had said in his animated sales pitch. He stood up and walked around the tractor for another inspection, kicking the tyres the way men do when they are contemplating buying a vehicle.

"I will come up first thing tomorrow morning to collect it," he announced decisively.

"No, no, that won't be possible," John countered adamantly, "I will drive it over at lunchtime." He did not give a reason, but we assumed he needed the tractor to finish off some fencing work before parting with it. We watched as the vehicle chuntered off down the lane and into the distance with little puffs of smoke rising intermittently as it wove its way through the country lanes toward *Bryn Awel*. I met Philip's gaze and he knew what I was thinking.

"I know, I know," he said defensively, shrugging his broad shoulders. "But he sounded genuine this time; I won't part with any money until I have the keys and documents in my hands," he promised.

"Well, let's hope you are right," I frowned back at him; I did not want to dampen his enthusiasm, but really, we were still smarting from the affair of the rotovator!

The cold afternoon air was unusually still and quiet with just the distant sound of the ducks on the lake, the bleating of lambs and the replies of their mothers as they called to each other. Up at the top of Mynydd Mechell, we could hear the little tractor as it puffed its way into the yard of *Bryn Awel* and stopped.

"Bleddyn Roberts, at *Tyddyn Gwyrdd* will be happy to sell you some red diesel," John Owen told Philip when he and his son, Aled, delivered the tractor the next day. Philip knew that red-coloured diesel fuel was used for off-road vehicles, especially agricultural machinery and was considerably cheaper as it was exempt from taxation. We did not really know Mr and Mrs Roberts, whose farm was on the Mountain Road, but they seemed friendly enough and we always exchanged waves as we passed, although we had never spoken. According to John Owen, the couple was locally known as *Di-Dor* or 'Non-Stop' as they worked all hours and so very hard on their farm. However, it was not only due to the amount of effort they put in that made them such successful farmers. It was also their local knowledge, handed down through the generations that included the consideration of their animals, the climate and the soil. Their farm, like the rest of Mynydd Mechell, was festooned with golden gorse and purple heather; however, their grassy pastures were like verdant green rivers, which wove their way between the colourful rocky outcrops. The sheep and cattle that grazed them were always in excellent condition, well suited to their environment.

"Bore da," Philip called out, as he entered the pristine farmyard of *Tyddyn Gwyrdd*. Mr Roberts, who emerged from one of the farm buildings, looked warily at the two empty five-gallon drums that Philip had placed on the ground to offer a handshake and introduce himself. *"Sut y dych chi*, Mr Roberts?" Philip continued, hoping that his efforts at a Welsh greeting might soften the frosty reception he was receiving. Mr Roberts reluctantly exchanged a handshake after finishing wiping his hands at a leisurely pace on the white linen cloth he was holding.

"And what would your business be here, Mr Barlow?" Mr Roberts asked, eyeing the empty drums suspiciously.

"Ah, yes," Philip replied nervously. "I just bought a tractor from

John Owen at *Bryn Awel* and he said you would be happy to sell me some red diesel for it." Philip smiled broadly at Mr Roberts, convinced that he would be pleased to have a customer. Mr Roberts' eyes narrowed at the mention of the name of John Owen and his lips tightened visibly. He said nothing for a few moments while fixing Philip with a thoughtful stare, and then to Philip's relief, Mr Roberts turned and with a gesture of his head, beckoned him to follow him to the diesel tank near the front gate, where Philip had left the microbus.

'Not a man given to many words,' Philip decided. When the two drums were filled and the money exchanged, Philip offered his hand again as he said goodbye. However, Mr Roberts' dark eyes lowered and locked with Philips' almost threateningly, and his lined, smile-less face was rigid with an absence of cordiality as he kept up rubbing his diesel-stained hands on the linen cloth.

"You will not be coming back again, will you, Mr Barlow?" Philip felt a flush of confusion at his words. "Next time you want diesel you will go to the *Esso* at Tregele, won't you?" Mr Roberts asked the question more as a poorly concealed command and escorted Philip to the gate.

As Philip loaded the drums of diesel into the open doorway of the microbus and watched Bleddyn Roberts retreat to his farm buildings, it dawned on him that he had been tricked again by that rascally John Owen!

10 The Fox Hunters

"We are coming up to shoot the foxes!" Philip had been so engrossed in his task of fitting the fixings on the post ready to take the new field gate he had made, that he had not heard the approach of the man with the shotgun tucked under his arm.

"You what?" Philip responded, shocked by the lack of formal introduction.

"The others will be coming soon," the man continued as he pulled out his lighter and lit a cigarette. "OK with you?" he asked as an afterthought. Philip scanned the lane to see who these 'others' were who were supposed to be coming soon.

"I'm sorry, who are you?" he asked.

"Oh, right. Yes, you must be the new owner here." The man put his lighter back in the pocket of his anorak and took a long draw on his cigarette. "Colin Hewitt. We do this every year."

'That is not a local accent,' Philip thought as he scrutinised the man, 'not even a Welsh name. He is just doing this for the sport!'

"Nice piece of land you have here," Colin Hewitt commented as he looked around at the fencing work that Philip had been doing. "Keeping sheep, eh? Had any trouble with foxes so far?"

"No, we haven't even seen any," Philip replied.

"Well they are about, you can be sure," the man warned, perusing the landscape for victims. "You will know about them if you want to keep chickens or geese."

Philip frowned as he considered the offer the man had made, but he had had some unique encounters with foxes, which made him reluctant to agree to their elimination. He thought back to the time when he was clearing out a deep ditch on a farm in the Weald of Kent. The sound of baying foxhounds had come first and then the bugles. The fox hunt was coming toward him at a noisy, excitable pace through the nearby fields of wheat stubble, while the barking of the hounds was growing louder and louder. Philip had stopped his digging and was waiting for that noisy procession to appear when he noticed a very frightened young vixen running for her life along the ditch toward him. She stopped about four yards away and, as their eyes met, Philip understood her unspoken question. 'Are you my friend or enemy?'

Saffron

"All that noise, just for little you?" He had looked pityingly down at the little red fox, who returned his gaze with a look of terror in her sweet and appealing eyes. Stepping to the side of the narrow channel, Philip had watched her as she trotted over his feet and quickly splashed her way up the stream of water. Following the line of the overgrown ditch Philip was in the process of clearing, she disappeared into the undergrowth of a small copse as the shouts from the hunters intensified and the thundering of the horses' hooves pounded closer on the frosty land.

"Hey! You! My man! Where did the fox go? Did you see it?" The man in the red coat and white jodhpurs astride the restless black horse pushed his riding helmet back with the tip of his horse crop. His face was taut; there was the thrill of bloodlust in his eyes and impatience in his voice.

"I'm not telling you where she went," Philip had replied with a defiant smile.

"Peasant!" spat the man, along with some unrepeatable expletives! Philip had watched as the arrogant man gasped in irritation, slapped his horse with his crop and galloped off in the wrong direction.

The memory of that trusting little fox had stayed with him ever since, so now, confronted with what seemed to Philip to be a similar situation, he did not feel it was a difficult decision to make.

"No, I'm sorry, Mr Hewitt, but I will not allow you to hunt on my land," he stated resolutely. Colin Hewitt was surprised and angry to hear Philip's decision; he straightened up and gave him a reproachful stare.

"You will regret that decision!" He replied belligerently, tucking his shotgun firmly under his arm and throwing the remains of his cigarette on the ground to emphasize his challenge. Turning his back on Philip, he stamped his way back down the lane to meet up with 'the others', who had just reached the gate leading to *Tŷ'n Llain*. "You will regret it!" he repeated over his shoulder.

"What have you done, Philip?" John Owen's words were ringing in Philip's ears as we lay in bed that night. "Those hunters have been coming here for years; they are friends of mine. Foxes are cruel; they do so much damage, Philip!" John had warned him scornfully. However, as he drifted off to sleep, Philip relived the moment when he had witnessed the most magical sight.

He had been pruning apple trees at Perry Hill in East Sussex during the early years of our marriage; the day was bitterly cold and the snow had settled thigh-deep and sparkling the night before, leaving an untouched white blanket covering the orchard where he was working. He had suddenly become aware of some movement and saw a pair of foxes, just three rows of apple trees away, one of them a beautifully sleek and glossy black vixen and the other a handsome red-brown stocky male. They were frolicking through the snow like two lovers, oblivious of Philip's fascinated gaze. Leaping playfully at each other, they rolled in the dry snow, chasing one another and making patterns in the crisp, glittering whiteness. Philip had been mesmerised; it was a vision he would never forget.

The foreboding words of the fox hunters haunted Philip's thoughts over the next few days as he kept working on the diamond-braced gate and hung it successfully on the gatepost. Over the following weekends, we could hear gunshots coming from the fields around *Llyn Bwch*, after which the carcasses of the foxes that were killed were thrown up into the hawthorn trees on the boundary surrounding our land. We were afraid to allow the children out to play and we kept Poppy tethered to her kennel in case she wandered off the farm and got herself into trouble.

"Tom Pratt has lost his geese to the foxes, Philip!" John Owen announced on the telephone. "Will you please come over? I want you to see it." Philip was suitably shocked by the sight of the three headless geese, which lay in the yard of John's English neighbour, dark red blood staining their snowy white feathers.

"Didn't even eat them," Tom said sadly. John looked at Philip with what he took to be a reproachful scowl, as though he had personally caused this massacre because of his refusal to allow the fox hunters on our land.

Philip thought deeply about the grizzly sight of Tom's geese as he went about his daily work on the fencing. He recalled fondly the time when a trusting and desperate little vixen had approached our picnic table in the New Forest in Hampshire. Her teats were swollen with milk and her appealing eyes had met mine, mother to mother, as she took morsels of food from my hands, retreating quickly to the woods, where her offspring would have been nestled safely. What to do, he asked himself; would Tom Pratt's geese not have been killed if he had permitted the fox hunters to hunt on our land? Should that bloodthirsty fox have been among those whose carcasses had been tossed into the hawthorn trees before it had the opportunity to do 'damage', just as John had warned? It seemed unjust that all the foxes needed to be killed in case some of them misbehaved. What is the right balance between the love of Nature and the love of killing Nature?

11 Dangerous Encounters

As a young girl in Secondary School, I chose to walk the hour to school with my sisters, rather than take the bus. Whether it was because I needed the exercise, enjoyed the social interaction with the friends we met along the way, or to save the bus fare to spend on goodies from the local sweet shop, I sometimes wonder. Our route took us along the busy Cuxton Road, up Northcote Road, and then, crossing the Roman-built Watling Street, we walked the seemingly never-ending Western Road, which took us to Frindsbury. Eventually, we climbed the steep Frindsbury Hill at top speed, hoping to make it to the school gates before the 9 o'clock bell rang, announcing the start of school and the appearance of the prefects at the school gate to take the names of latecomers, sentencing them to detention.

I would like to say that the experience gave me a lifelong habit of punctuality, but that would not be true. However, the exercise, I am sure, contributed to my ability to keep a good healthy pace in later life, in what was to become my very demanding role as a busy mother and a farmer's wife.

At some time during those years, we heard the shocking news of the tragic accident of a woman who lived in one of the new estates we would have passed on our daily march up and down Frindsbury Hill. A young mother was walking her little boy to playschool through one of the alleyways and the little lad had run on happily ahead. However, he was shocked and bewildered when he turned and saw that his mother had simply disappeared! A deep sinkhole had suddenly opened in the ground, and she had fallen into a seemingly bottomless cavern, never to be seen again.

Frindsbury and its surrounding areas were abuzz with the news of the tragedy. News reporters visited to interview the locals who had known the woman and the dreadful event was given a lot of coverage on TV. Investigators came to the scene, while some unfortunates had the job of abseiling down the shaft to see if they could find the missing mother. However, try as they may, they could not reach the bottom, so after a few weeks, with not a sound from below, no hope and no reason, it was decided that nothing more could be done. The alleyway was sealed off, an enormous amount of concrete was poured into the hole and some lessons were learned from the experience (so they said). The TV reporters dwindled, the hype died down and the chatter on the demise of the hapless woman steadily became just a mumbled whisper in the archives of the history of Frindsbury, never again to be brought to mind, or so I thought.

Mr and Mrs Case were an English couple who kept a very pretty, tidy garden around their whitewashed stone cottage named *Bryn Egor*, which we passed on our walks down the well-worn track leading from *Tŷ'n Llain* to the Mountain Road. Mr Case reminded us of a 'Brigadier' type of person due to his stature and comportment. He was a congenial elderly man with a good crop of white hair and a heavy moustache, stained on its edges by tobacco from the old pipe that he smoked. Mrs Case, on the other hand, kept some dark colour in her luxuriant head of hair and was evidently the keen gardener of the household, as she was often seen busy tending it. Although we had introduced ourselves quite early on, we knew very little about their history, until one morning at the beginning of March. We were walking down the lane to meet up with my parents, who were coming to collect Joshua and I to take us to Holyhead market. Amelia was entranced by their happy little West Highland Terrier, Tammy, who trotted out to greet us as we approached the double gates of *Bryn Egor*, followed by her two enthusiastic companions. One was a black and white Springer and the other was a fine specimen of a Cocker spaniel with a silken coat in cream and red/gold. The Cocker had a strange tilt to his head, which was at a constant horizontal angle and we wondered if he had been run over at some time.

"No, no, nothing like that; the vet says it is inner-ear trouble, but he seems to get by and doesn't appear to be in any pain," explained Mrs Case. A small grey Shetland gelding called Diesel had paused in his pursuit of delectable pasture in the back garden, gracing us with a few moments of interest. We learned that Diesel, unlike Jeffrey, was a docile little pony and that Mr and Mrs Case came from Kent. "Oh, you wouldn't know the place; it is called Frindsbury," Mrs Case assured us. I replied that I was very familiar with Frindsbury as I went to school there.

"Well, we moved here about fifteen years ago to get away from Frindsbury," Mrs Case continued, oblivious of my interjection. "My sister had a terrible accident and we lost her. She fell into a big hole that opened in one of the alleyways of her estate as she was taking her little boy to playschool. It was so difficult to live there with all the sad memories and with everyone talking about it, so we decided to move as far away as possible to where no one would even have heard about it." Philip and I looked at each other and he began to shuffle his feet noisily on the rough and stony ground. He had heard the story frequently from my family of the lady who had fallen down the hole.

"That is so sad," I commiserated tactfully. "I am so sorry to hear about that, Mrs Case." Thankfully, just at that moment, my parents arrived in their red Mercedes estate car and we hastily took our leave. Behind every door, there is a story to tell and the tragic end of Mrs Case's sister is one that is indelibly embedded in my memory. Since then there have been so many news reports of 'sinkholes' opening in various places worldwide, making the problem a modern-day phenomenon.

The weather was particularly harsh all the following week; cold, wet and extremely windy. Cheerful daffodils, bedecked in either snowy-white or sunny yellow, had begun to appear the week before, but now the savage wind had dashed their lovely little faces relentlessly into the ground, leaving them all muddy, tattered and torn. It was during that week that our Welsh Mountain ewes started to give birth to gorgeous, fluffy, white lambs, a circumstance that was met by one and all with awe and wonder. The children's faces were a picture when they came down to breakfast one morning to discover a new-born lamb, wrapped in a towel and peeping out from the open door of the Rayburn's warming oven.

"I found it when I did the rounds of the fields at first light this morning," Philip informed us. "It must have been born overnight; it would have died if it had stayed there any longer."

"Did its mother abandon it?" I asked.

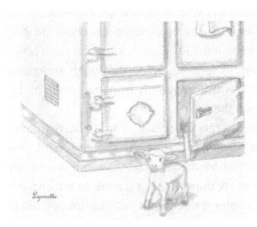
Lynnette

"No, no," Philip assured me. "She followed me down to the barn, whickering to her lamb all the way and that is where she is now. I will take the lamb to her when it has warmed up a bit; thankfully, it looks as if they had enough time to bond. If her devotion is anything to go by, these Welsh ewes should make excellent mothers; I only hope the little fella recovers." Just then, the frail little lamb with its rust-coloured collar running across the back of its neck pushed

92

its way out of the warming oven and onto the kitchen floor. Standing shakily on its wobbly little legs for a few seconds, it looked nervously around, and then began calling for its mother. We were all delighted!

Thankfully, the weather was more hospitable by the time I was due for my regular trip to Holyhead market with my parents and it was Philip's turn to be the teacher for the day. The Education Officer had come to visit us shortly after we moved in and had agreed to support us in home-schooling our children. I had been enjoying teaching them Art and English language, which, along with needlework and French had been among my favourite topics and in which I had gained School Certificates.

Philip's forté was Maths, Science, Horticulture and Geography, besides a host of other practical capabilities. Although having left school illiterate, he had put tremendous effort into learning to read, while, due to his incredible photographic memory, he had absorbed abundant information on his favourite topics. I often wondered why Philip had such difficulty in reading aloud, although he never gave up trying. At the breakfast table, the children and I listened as Philip managed to read us a small portion of the Bible. After a short discussion and application, it was time for another cup of tea and on with the day. Refilling the teapot over the sink, I allowed my gaze to wander out of the window, almost scalding myself with the hot water as I was distracted by the scene that presented itself before me.

"Oh, no!" I exclaimed. "Athaliah sheep is in Jeffrey's field!" The chatter at the table halted abruptly and several little jam-covered faces turned in my direction, while Philip joined me at the window to see what was going on. At that moment, Jeffrey horse cantered over from the far corner of his paddock to inspect his visitor, like a giant black spider that had just noticed he had caught a fly in his web. Philip began to chuckle, the children abandoned their toast and gathered around the kitchen sink, trying to see through the window.

"This could be the best lesson she has learned yet!" Philip said with a cheeky smile on his face and a wicked twinkle in his eyes.

Knowing that horses are strictly vegetarian, we had no worries that he would try to eat her, so everyone returned to the table, allowing Athaliah sheep to discover Jeffrey's evil temper for herself. Glancing through the window a little later, I could see Athaliah standing quite still, several feet from the stone wall over which she had entered the paddock, with Jeffrey making slow and menacing circles around her.

The conversation at the breakfast table turned to what subjects Daddy/teacher would be teaching that day. Joshua did not feel he needed to be part of the discussion about Maths and Geography (whatever they were) and was busy making 'roadways' through the scattered toast crumbs on the table with his little jammy fingers.

"Do you think I should take him with me today?" I suggested, wondering if he might get rather bored with the lessons. Philip has an enviable capacity for general knowledge, being able to give an in-depth answer to any question on any subject, which was always accurate and informative. I doubted, however, that it would appeal to the wandering attention span of a four-year-old. In fact, bedtime stories read from books discussing the difference between edible and poisonous mushrooms would often have the children calling out to me for mercy! Philip assures me that he was only teasing them, for they loved to hear him read from Rudyard Kipling, the Tales of Narnia, or Paddington Bear.

"No, he will be fine, don't worry," he replied. "He can play with some of his toys in the corner if he gets bored. Anyway, you have a special reason for going to the market today." He gave me a knowing look and a wink as I started to clear away the table. Yes,

I had put down a deposit on a beautiful red corduroy doll's pram for Amelia, a metallic blue bicycle for Daniel and a bright yellow go-kart for Joshua. That day I was going to put down some more money on our prize and then, hopefully, the following week I would be able to bring them back to store at my parents' home until the day of our wedding anniversary party.

"Oh, dear." Philip had stopped rinsing jam from his hands at the sink and was standing stock still and staring out of the window. "I think Jeffrey horse has just killed her!" he said, his face shocked and wooden and his eyes wide with disbelief. "I only expected him to chase her around a bit until she jumped back into her own field." We all charged back to the window and sure enough, Athaliah sheep was lying on her back, with Jeffrey horse standing over her, chewing at her limp, outstretched neck!

"Oh, my word!" I exclaimed. "We stood by and let him kill her!"

"I had better go and see what I can do!" Philip turned abruptly, pulled on his wax jacket that was hanging on the back door and searched for his tweed hat that he had stuffed into the pockets. "Where did I leave my boots?" he asked rhetorically. Deciding that he had left them at the front door, he disappeared rapidly through the door leading to the main part of the house and out of the front door.

"We stood by and let him kill her!" My own words hammered at my conscience as I stared helplessly at the scene through the window, where the poor creature was being devoured by that horrible Shetland pony! I came to my senses and decided to use the only effective weapon I had to contribute to the cause from that distance. Throwing open the back door, I yelled with all my might in the direction of the crime.

"Jeffrey horse, you leave that sheep alone!" Unfortunately, I had not noticed Philip, whose boots had been at the back door, not the front as he had assumed and who was now bent down below my frame of vision, still pulling them on. I became aware of his presence as he rose with controlled dignity from his crouched position to his full height and, with his tweed hat slightly askew, he gave me a look of patient endurance.

"Was that necessary?" he asked quietly, but I could tell that he was in a degree of shock from my seismic vocal blast!

"Ooh, sorry," I grimaced, watching as he went striding off, over the concrete stile leading to Jeffrey's paddock to see what he could salvage of poor Athaliah sheep. Galvanised into action, I grabbed my padded purple coat from off the back door, tugged my *snood* down around my ears and piled into my boots. Daniel had already run to fetch his brown anorak and was searching for a matching pair among the pile of discarded rubber boots outside the backdoor, ready to run up in support of his Daddy, while Amelia had decided to do the same.

"We stood by and let him kill her!" I repeated, my self-reproaching words pounding in my head with every beat of my boots on the hard ground as I raced up the field toward Jeffrey's paddock. We all stopped and stood still at the wall of the paddock, watching with anticipation to see what Philip would do next.

Climbing gingerly over the barbed wire topping the stone wall, he managed to wave the brute away authoritatively while he edged toward the limp form of Athaliah sheep. With Jeffrey dancing around irritably close by, Philip very gently lifted the woolly body and carried her toward the field boundaries. Her head lolled lifelessly and we felt all hope of her survival drain away as he laid her on our side of the wall before climbing back over it himself. Much to our surprise, however, the instant the sheep was released, she seemed to spring back into life! Leaping firmly onto her feet, she shook her head a few times, and then staggered away to graze.

"She's alive!" Daniel and Amelia chorused, with relief and

wonder. "Athaliah sheep is alive!" They repeated, holding hands and jumping up and down on the spot with joy.

"That is not Athaliah sheep," Philip stated as he strolled over to join the happy group.

"What?" We all replied in shocked unison.

"No, that is not Athaliah sheep," he assured us. Philip had studied his sheep carefully during the short time we had owned them, getting to know them all well and he certainly had plenty of opportunities to get to know Athaliah sheep particularly well.

"Well, who is she then?" I asked as we all watched her grazing contentedly, with not a mark or bloodstain on her to tell of her 'ordeal' with Jeffrey horse.

"I don't know who she is, but she is not one of ours; maybe she is just a free-spirited wanderer who found herself in the wrong place at the wrong time," Philip suggested, genuinely bewildered but in no doubt of his verdict. "She has no earmarks to identify her, she wasn't shorn last year and she is heavily pregnant," he announced with certainty. "But I have a pretty good idea that

Saffron

Jeffrey horse had romantic ideas toward her," he proffered with that impish grin that settled attractively into his beard when he was being mischievous.

With the drama over, we strolled contemplatively back down to the house to find little Joshua by the back door, struggling into his rubber boots. He had spent the entire time since we left the kitchen correctly applying the obligatory zip-up coat, gloves and bobble hat that he knew I insisted on before going out in the cold. I picked him up and gave him a big hug for being such a good boy, feeling sad that, in the panic of the moment, I had completely forgotten about my little man, who no doubt would have wanted to see what was going on. However, he assured me that he had been watching from the bedroom window while dressing and had seen it all.

"Did the naughty horse bite the sheep, Mummy?" he asked.

"No, Darling, he was just kissing her," I replied comfortingly.

"He did bite her," Joshua assured me, nodding sagely.

"Really?" I asked. "How do you know?"

"Because I saw crumbs dropping out of his mouth!" he answered, wagging his little finger to add emphasis to his assertion.

Well, how could one argue with that? We returned our attention to Jeffrey horse as he cavorted around his paddock, kicking up turf in annoyance like a lusty and frustrated lover. What a day that object of his amorous advances was having, I thought as we all watched her through the kitchen window. First, she was mistaken for a female Shetland pony by Jeffrey horse. Then she had been accused of being some other sheep by this character in a green wax jacket and now being Joshua's idea of an oversized biscuit! Could it get any worse? In fact, it did.

The very next day, that flirtatious madam was back in the field, tantalising poor Jeffrey with her charms. That was not the last time either, so after a few more times of Philip having to 'rescue' her from her own mischief, he decided to confine her with the original Athaliah sheep in the walled pen beside the old barn. There she stayed until she produced healthy, part-Suffolk twins, which kept her distracted enough so as not to bother her disappointed Shetland 'boyfriend' again. The children decided to call her Dozy Nora and her lambs, Dora and Bobby.

12 The Wedding Anniversary Party

"I am sorry Mr Davies, but I just cannot contain one of those sheep that you brought us. I am sure that she is more antelope than sheep and I don't know what else to do with her!" Philip was leaning against the wall in the hallway as he spoke with Mr Davies on the telephone. Mr Davies sounded undaunted and frankly quite amused by the dilemma that Philip had found himself in with his ongoing battle with Athaliah sheep.

"Well she sounds like just the sort of sheep that would do well to roam and forage here in the mountains," he replied. "You know, they need to be survivors for this kind of terrain. I can collect her tomorrow and swap her for a more docile sheep if you like?" Philip was relieved at the prospect of ridding himself of the daily nightmare of trying to outsmart 'that wretched sheep'. Still, there was another matter that he had not considered when agreeing to Mr Davies' proposal.

"Tomorrow is our wedding anniversary party, Philip," I reminded him, wondering how he could have forgotten after all the weeks of planning. Philip looked at me after putting down the telephone and took a moment to compute the situation.

"Don't worry, Love," he attempted to reassure me. "Mr Davies won't be staying long; his visit won't disturb our party."

I hoped not; the children and I had put a lot of effort into decorating the kitchen with paper streamers and pretty pictures they had produced during their art lessons. I had even laboriously scrubbed and cleaned the 'diagonal green trail' from the kitchen carpet and was hoping that it would be dry enough to walk on by the next day. My parents were due to join us for the special event at lunchtime, bringing gifts for the children, including the items they had helped me to collect from Holyhead market.

"No, no, we will be fine," Philip repeated and I wondered if he was trying to convince himself more than me that he had not forgotten our special day. I decided to give him the benefit of the doubt and say no more about the matter; I knew how he had agonised over that sheep and how he hated the thought of being defeated by a woolly-faced renegade!

The anticipated day dawned and the children came to the breakfast table with an air of secrecy and excitement. A little murmur between them indicated that they had organised a surprise for us.

"Surprise!" they announced enthusiastically, as they laid a pile of homemade anniversary cards before us.

"Oh, what a lovely thought, how kind," I exclaimed, nudging Philip to attention. I could tell that his mind was distracted by his conversation with Mr Davies the previous evening and with the pressing matter of finishing the fencing.

"Oh, yes. Lovely!" Philip agreed, picking up one of the homemade envelopes placed on his tea plate.

"That is my one Daddy," Amelia confirmed, tugging at her Daddy's arm, a sweet smile decorating her cute, impish face. "Are you going to open it?"

"Yes, of course," he replied, carefully peeling back the sticky tape from the blue envelope to reveal the loving words and the carefully drawn pictures on the card within. Amelia had always adored her Daddy and deep down wanted to be just like him when she grew up. She anticipated his delight at receiving her loving letter of congratulations and he did not disappoint.

"Oh, how lovely, Amelia," he said, passing her masterpiece to me for approval. "A very nice picture of you with Poppy," he suggested, hoping he had guessed right. Amelia's little blond eyebrows came together in a disgruntled frown.

"No," she replied, somewhat offended. "It is you with 'that wretched sheep' you keep chasing."

Philip's lips tightened and he raised his eyebrows at me; I could tell what he was thinking from the look on his face: 'That sheep has to go. She is damaging my reputation and I will be pleased to see the back of her today!'

"So, let's have some breakfast," I suggested, as the last of the colourful creations had been paraded and appreciated. "Then, when Nanny and Granddad come, we will have some surprises for you."

The children loved their new toys, which arrived with their grandparents, and they ran outside instantly to play with them until lunchtime. It was good to have the company of my parents for the event and it was a rare occasion to have my father come to visit. He had been quite a social character in his younger years, leading to success in his many enterprising ventures as a businessman. Nowadays, however, he was becoming increasingly reclusive, preferring to stay at home in Cemaes, where he spent his days just sitting in his rocking chair, watching through the bedroom window at the tide washing in and out of the bay.

My mother, on the other hand, was the life and soul of the party, always happy to join in whatever fun was on offer. She had been a very hard-working wife and mother; her strong moral values that had formed the core of her family were passed on to the families of her daughters. Dad's shrewd, resourceful business mind, along with Mum's industriousness and sense of humour had kept the family afloat during those difficult times, while their love and generosity had kept us all close. Now, here was my mother at the meal table with a paper party hat balanced crookedly on her head, sipping some homemade wine she had brought to share and making the children laugh. Philip and my Dad savoured the whisky that Philip had gratefully received from them as his anniversary gift, while the smell of roast chicken and roast potatoes wafted from the Rayburn, filling the kitchen with a tantalising aroma.

Mum's amazing Yorkshire puddings were the highlight of the meal and were almost matched by her contribution of sherry trifle.

We were all just in that contented state of repletion and my father was looking like he was ready to go home for his afternoon nap when a vehicle pulled up in the driveway. It was Mr Davies, of course! Philip had been anticipating his arrival throughout the meal and I had noticed his attention frequently wandering through the large picture window that faced the driveway. Tweed, the effervescent companion of Mr Davies, bounced from the cab of the truck, making himself at home by marking his territory and ingratiating himself with my mother, who fell instantly in love with him. He was eager to show off his skills as a sheepdog, but it was not necessary since the replacement for Athaliah was a timid contrast to her and was led compliantly into the field where the other sheep were grazing. She took a few paces, and then stood still, gazing around to assess her new surroundings. Spotting the flock grazing contentedly at the bottom of the field in the lee of the gorse hedging, she made her way tentatively towards them. She had no problem integrating, as she would have known those sheep from when they all ran the mountains of Bethesda together.

It was a reasonably pleasant day, so my Dad donned his jacket and flat cap and joined us as we leaned over the wooden field gate, watching our new arrival. *Llyn Bwch* was sparkling dark blue that day as the wind played on its surface and a flock of ducks swooped down onto the lake to add to the disturbance. Mr Davies seemed pleased to see some lambs amongst our sheep.

"Did you have any problems with the lambing?" he asked, squinting into the bright sunshine.

"One or two were difficult," Philip replied, as he mentally relived the anxieties he had felt about venturing into this new line of experience. "But I took your advice and went on a lambing course, thank you." Mr Davies studied Philip's large hands, lying heavily on the gate; perfect for fencing and many other things requiring strength, but he winced visibly at the thought of those hands playing midwife to some poor ewe in birthing distress.

"Maybe your wife should go on the course," he suggested, smiling at me.

"Maybe next year," Philip replied, for we had a little secret that we were about to announce just before Mr Davies' arrival. Athaliah distracted our attention at that moment; she was very disgruntled about being cooped up in her pen and was making quite a fuss about it.

"So, is this the renegade that has been causing all the trouble?" Mr Davies glanced sympathetically at Philip as the three men shifted to lean on the gate to her enclosure. Athaliah bucked skittishly at the attention, making several circuits of the pen and a few unsuccessful attempts to scale the walls.

"Perfect!" Mr Davies exclaimed, smiling broadly. "She will be ideal for what I need; I don't know how I managed to miss her value as a mountain sheep before. Still, I did say I would give you my best." He grinned at Philip, but Philip was in no mood for levity on the matter of Athaliah sheep!

"So," Mr Davies thought it wise to change the subject. "I have a suggestion for you," he said as he turned and gestured toward his truck, which was attracting the attention of a small gathering of Nanny, Poppy and children. "You really need a sheepdog," he continued, as we moved across to join the excitement and to see what was in the back of the truck. Cowering in the dark recesses of the cage, we could make out the form of a very timid Border collie.

"*Tid yma, Cil!*" Mr Davies commanded as he slid back the bolt on the cage door. As the collie emerged reluctantly at his firm urgings into the daylight, we recognised her as the dog we had seen in the corner of one of Mr Davies' sheds when we had visited his farm.

Despite her timidity and the fact that she could have done with a good bath, we all thought her to be quite beautiful. Her long coat was a red-brown with patches of creamy white on her paws and muzzle and she looked rather like a large fox with her long bushy tail. Her ears stood erect and almost back-to-back when she heard Mr Davies call her name.

"*Cil, ewch lawr!*" He spoke kindly, but with authority and after several uncertain attempts, she jumped from the truck and stood shakily on the driveway as directed. Tweed had shown a total lack of interest in Poppy, who had been following him devotedly around the property since he had arrived. However, he now moved in reassuringly by the side of this lovely *debutante,* who warmed to his presence as he circled her a few times, sniffing and giving her a final inspection. Mr Davies ordered Tweed away before repeating his command.

"*Cil, ewch lawr!*" and she dropped obediently to a lying position on the grass, awaiting her master's next order. Despite all of us strangers staring at her and with her coat a matted tangle of mud and farm debris, she still managed to strike a dignified pose. With her ears pricked up and attentive and with her long front legs arranged neatly together before her, she had the presence of a regal Sphinx. Her haunches were broad, yet delicate and her dirty, white-tipped tail twitched nervously on the grass as she returned our scrutiny.

"Just ten months old and she is pregnant, I must tell you...." I just caught the end of Mr Davies telling us her story.

"And the father of her pups?" Philip asked, but the answer to that question was quite evident. Mr Davies gestured toward his trusty companion, Tweed, who was striking the same pose as *Cil,* just a few feet away, but never taking his eyes off her.

"They will be fine, strong pups you can be sure," Mr Davies was giving *Cil* an excellent recommendation, but he did not need to convince his audience; we were already sold!

"Well, I had wondered what to give you as a special anniversary gift," I said, as Philip and I cleared up the kitchen after tea that evening.

"No, no, I was very pleased with the nice jumper you gave me," he replied indulgently.

"Sixty pounds; I hope she is worth it for you," I mused, wondering how the dog would be feeling about her new home in the old barn that night. "Do you think it was a good price to pay for her?"

"Mr Davies has always been fair with us," Philip affirmed. "Anyway, I would have paid him sixty pounds just to take that awful sheep away!" he stated with passion. "I only hope the new sheep won't be nearly as much trouble."

With the day's happy celebrations completed, the children bathed and put to bed and the kitchen looking less like the tail end of market day, I reached for the kettle and started making up the bottles of milk to feed Nora's orphan lambs. It was sad that she had survived for only a few days after the birth of her twins, but they had been born where they would be loved and cared for and she had been able to supply them with the vital colostrum they needed to be strong and healthy.

"How about we finish off our special day by sitting and enjoying a drink together when everything is done?" I suggested; the thought of a romantic evening alone appealed.

"Sorry, Love, but I cannot leave my new dog filthy dirty in the barn overnight, I need to bathe her," he answered.

"Tonight! You have to bathe her tonight?" I was quite shocked by this revelation! "She has been in that state for months by the look of her, how about bathing her tomorrow?"

"No, sorry, but it has to be done tonight," Philip affirmed with that air of finality that meant the matter was now closed.

We stood facing each other across the kitchen, hard-headed Saxon, versus quick-tempered Jute, in some kind of cross-cultural standoff!

The vision of a romantic evening with my battle-weary warrior ended abruptly as I watched him pull on his wax jacket and tweed hat, search the cupboard for the torch and disappear into the darkness.

"Do you think you could run a bath for her?" he asked, adding insult to my disappointment, as he popped his head back in through the back door. I gave him a hard stare through the kitchen window as he strode past it on his way to the old barn. He was completely oblivious of my angst, however, as he was absorbed in his efforts to keep his hat firmly pulled down on his head and his coat collar gripped tightly around his neck against the wind and rain that challenged his progress. I was certainly not feeling serene and *Sphinx-like* at that very moment!

"Glass of wine, Philip?" I offered from the dark and creepy space just inside the door of the old barn. 'If you can't beat them, join them', my Dad always said.

"No, I am OK thanks," Philip replied from the dimly illuminated depths of the barn, where a shadeless and dusty light bulb hung from a dubious-looking ancient black wire.

Taking another sip of my orange juice while sitting awkwardly on my uncomfortable, upturned beer crate, I watched the two orphan lambs stagger away to their straw beds, their milk bottles empty and their little tummies full and satisfied.

"I think I will call her Jill," Philip announced, as he brushed the knots and tangles from his newly bathed dog with one of my old hairbrushes. "It sounds like _Cil_ but is more English."

"You know, this little dog has never known what it is like to be part of a family," he mused, still brushing and grooming her. "I don't want her to be just a working farm dog; I want her to also be our family pet. What do you think?" I looked across at 'Jill', who was possibly having her first grooming ever in her ten months of life. Watching the tenderness with which Philip handled her and the fear and confusion in her eyes, I began to feel pity for her.

"Maybe we could give her a few days to get used to us, and then make her a bed beside Poppy in the kitchen," Philip suggested.

"Maybe we should," I conceded. The scurry of a rat or two could be heard amongst the hay bales, upon which sat Dinky-Doo, the farm cat, who eyed the invasion of her _boudoir_ with notable disapproval. Outside the wind began to howl eerily.

"Happy Anniversary, Philip," I said.

"Happy Anniversary, Love," he replied.

13 Runaway Teddy Bears

"Mummy's in bed because she's poorly."

"No, she's not, she's pregnance. When they makes you pregnance, then they makes you sick." Philip was leaning suavely against the bedroom door, holding my obligatory morning cup of tea while relating the conversation at the breakfast table that morning. We were hoping that this precious baby would be a little sister for Amelia.

"It isn't fair!" Amelia had protested. "Daniel and Joshua have a brother, but I don't have a sister." It seemed likely that she would get her wish since I was very fragile during this pregnancy, as I was while carrying Amelia, rather than robust and healthy as when carrying the boys. For that reason, home-schooling was becoming somewhat challenging, with the children often having their lessons on the floor of our bedroom as I rested in bed.

The Education officer had come to visit just the previous week and had warmly commended me for the comprehensive standard of learning to which the children had attained and had strongly encouraged that we continue.

"I was home-schooled on my parent's farm," he had disclosed. "I really believe it is the best way for a child to learn."

However, as much as I would have liked to continue, I knew that I was not able to keep the active pace needed to satisfy our energetic youngsters. Philip too was becoming increasingly busy with the farm and the growing flock size.

"I am sorry, Mr Williams," I had replied, knowing that he would be disappointed to hear we had decided to send the children to school with the new school term. "But I have to tell you that I am pregnant and...."

"You don't have to apologise to me; it isn't my fault!" Mr Williams had interrupted, with a mischievous, white-toothed grin

111

spreading impudently across his face. I felt a hot flush of embarrassment redden my face and I began to waffle defensively. However, he had been thoroughly amused by his own wit.

"Do you think you will be up to doing their lessons today?" Philip interrupted my thoughts as he pulled back the curtains and looked through the window at the lambs grazing beside their mothers in the field leading up to *Bryn Llyn*. "John Owen called in this morning and said he had just finished building a sheep dip for some new neighbours from England," he explained. "As Mr Davies recommended that we dip the sheep in April, I might walk over to meet them later today; maybe I could offer to give them a hand with their dipping and dip ours at the same time." I was not feeling particularly enthusiastic about smelly sheep dips at that delicate morning moment; I was more concerned about my cup of tea and wondering how I might survive as 'teacher' for that day.

"Anyway," Philip sounded blisteringly energetic, keen to get going on his day's work as he turned from the window and strode happily back toward the bedroom door. "As soon as you are ready, can you help me start the tractor?"

I could tell this was going to be a difficult day!

"Now children, I want you to draw this still life." It was quite late in the afternoon and I was exerting as much authority as I could muster after an exhausting day of home-schooling. The 'still life' was a collection of fruit and vegetables, which I had carefully arranged on the sideboard. "Now watch me as I show you how to do it," I instructed and set to work sketching on my art paper. Daniel was a willing student and loved to learn; in a short while, he had produced a suitable representation of the display and was searching amongst the array of pencils on the table to colour in his creation. Joshua was experimenting with a fistful of pencils, making colourful rainbows across his paper, which looked interesting but bore no relation to the subject at hand. Amelia was sharpening her pencil.

"Amelia Lucy, you have been sharpening your pencil for quite long enough!" I was beginning to lose my patience after half an hour of encouraging her to get started. "Now will you please draw this still life?" Amelia continued sharpening her pencil.

"I want to draw a ballerina," she announced calmly while examining the fine point on her pencil.

"Amelia," I persisted, "you can draw a ballerina later, but for now I want you to draw this still life." Amelia dropped her pencil on the table and threw herself dramatically face down across her blank paper, her little shoulders shaking with mock tears.

"I want to draw a ballerina." she sobbed.

I knew this would be a difficult day.

Daniel was used to Amelia's little tantrums when she could not get her way and continued, nonplussed with his colouring in. Joshua had paused in his artistic efforts and was watching with interest to see what I was going to do next. Amelia had been the easiest of our children to manage and was a sweet, gentle sister to her adored brothers. However, ever since she was a toddler, we knew she had quite a temper on her when things did not please her. Nevertheless, no, this would not do; I was the teacher today, so she must learn obedience.

"Amelia!" I said firmly, "I want you to draw this..." I gestured toward the 'still life', just as Joshua, who was evidently bored and had slipped down from his chair, pulled out an apple from underneath it, causing the whole display to tumble to the floor. I watched as he opened the back door and carefully closed it behind him, biting into his apple as he went. I turned to Daniel, who was colouring his green apple in a dark brown and I made a fleeting mental note to check that out for a possible colour blindness problem.

"Amelia," I said determinedly to the sad little figure, still lying prostrate across her paper. "I want you to draw…a ballerina."

"OK," she replied, sitting up, dry-eyed and smiling, and she drew a ballerina.

I was rather pleased when school was over that day.

"Right everyone, off to your bedrooms; please tidy your rooms and get ready for bed while I prepare your dinner," I instructed and started to tidy up the day's debris.

The kettle was bubbling on the Rayburn's hotplate and the dinner was all underway by the time Philip came in from visiting the new neighbours that he had mentioned that morning.

"Dave and Molly are their names," he said, between sips of tea as he sat at the table. "Nice couple…. retired…. come from Lancashire. I will take you up to meet them some time."

"What did they say about dipping the sheep?" I asked while folding the dry laundry that I had gathered from the washing line earlier in the day.

"No problem," Philip replied. "Dave damaged his back while he worked for the Post Office and isn't up to doing much himself, so he was glad of my offer of help. We will dip his sheep one day next week, then ours the following day."

"Ah, a good result for both of you then," I said, opening the kitchen door to take the basket of laundry up to the bedrooms, where I almost tripped over Amelia, who was standing just the other side of it. She was still fully dressed and carrying a stick over her shoulder with a bulging scarf tied to one end.

"Amelia!" I exclaimed, surprised that she was not in her pyjamas as instructed, yet relieved that I had not trampled her in my haste. "I told you to… What is the matter, Amelia?" Something was seriously wrong; she was not moving to let me pass and in the dim light of the hallway, I could make out a look of defiance on her little face.

"I am running away!" she stated, hoisting her stick more firmly onto her shoulder.

"Oh, are you?" I replied, mentally searching for any known tips on how to deal with such situations.

"Yes!" she replied resolutely.

"Well...um….would you like a cup of tea before you go?" I suggested, turning to put the basket of laundry back in the kitchen.

"All right," Amelia agreed, relaxing her stance and smiling. Following me, she swung her load off her shoulder, leaning it carefully against the chair onto which she climbed. As I looked at her, I felt a twinge of guilt and pity. I supposed it must be one thing to have a grumpy teacher that one could come home from school and tell Mummy all about, but it would be quite trying if one's grumpy teacher were the same grumpy Mummy at home.

"Amelia is going to run away, Daddy," I informed Philip, as I collected one of my best cups and a saucer from the cupboard.

"Is that right, Amelia?" Philip asked, looking up from his newspaper and studying his daughter indulgently. Amelia was kneeling on her chair and leaning her elbows on the kitchen table as she waited importantly for her cup of tea.

"Yes, I am!" she said emphatically, her blond ponytail with its tartan ribbon bouncing up and down as she nodded.

"I see, so where do you think you will go then?" Philip folded up his newspaper and gave Amelia a look of serious interest in her dilemma.

"I don't know yet, I haven't decided," she replied, folding her hands together and looking out through the window at the darkening sky.

"Would you like to look at my maps after our cup of tea then?" Philip asked and Amelia's face brightened.

"Yes, please!" she responded enthusiastically. The day was turning out better than she had expected. Not only was she having her own personal cup of tea with her parents' complete attention, but she was going to run away with her Daddy, who had suggested he should go with her to help her find her way in case she got lost.

"Should we take Mummy with us too?" Philip suggested as they both pored over the enormous map of the surrounding countryside that he had spread across the table. Amelia looked up at me through the curtain of steam, issuing from the vegetables cooking on the Rayburn and briefly considered the suggestion.

"No," she answered decisively; "she won't be able to climb over the fences and she will only slow us down."

"Hmmm; perhaps you are right," Philip conceded, eyeing my widening girth, for our baby was now beginning to show. "Anyway, it is getting too late to run away tonight and dinner is nearly ready; shall we run away tomorrow?"

"All right then," Amelia agreed happily. She gathered up her stick with its attached bundle (which I later discovered was full of her teddy bears), got herself ready for bed and nothing more was ever said about running away.

14 Dave and Molly

"So, do you want to come over and meet Dave and Molly this evening?" Philip asked the family at lunchtime as he finished his last spoonful of soup and reached for the tea still in his cup. His suggestion was met with enthusiasm by all the children around the table. "Then you must be good for Mummy this afternoon and tidy up your bedrooms before we go; isn't that right, Mummy?" Philip said, looking pleased with himself for supporting my cause that day. "I think you will like them, and they are looking forwards to meeting you," he added, putting his empty cup down on the table and striding back towards the back door.

It was an experience for the two little ones to venture beyond our acreage and explore new terrain in the outside world. Skipping happily ahead of us, they followed the path that led to the forbidden kissing gate with Poppy firmly under control on her lead. Daniel led the way confidently since he alone had been permitted to accompany his Dad and Jill to help with the sheep dipping at *Tŷ'n Gorse*. Jill, now heavy with puppies, bounded along excitedly beside them, her creamy-white-tipped tail swishing in wide circles as she went.

"Listen!" Philip said suddenly, stopping in his tracks and looking around him.

"What is it?" I asked in alarm and made an involuntary grab at his arm; the thought of snakes had not crossed my mind until that moment.

"Shhhhhh! Listen!" he said again and started looking up at the sky. "What can you hear?" Well, honestly, quite a few sounds were going on around us, such as the odd call of the ewes checking on the whereabouts of their offspring and the bleating of the lambs calling back to their mothers. I could hear the cuckoo not too far away, which was always a delight as it confirmed that spring had arrived. We must have disturbed a nesting Skylark along the way, for it was issuing cries of indignation as it hovered and fluttered high above us, showering us with its tapestry of clear notes and trills. The quarrelsome, noisy chatter of the Black Headed gulls roosting on *Llyn Bwch* was growing louder and more excitable as the numbers in their colonies began to swell.

"Isn't it all so musical?" Philip said romantically. "Like our own personal orchestra." Yes, it was delightful; a perfect way to forget the stress of the day as it tumbled into the perfect evening.

"John Owen has done an excellent job of the fencing, don't you think?" Philip asked as we approached the top of Mynydd Mechell and the farm belonging to Dave and Molly came into view.

"Did John do all of this?" I was genuinely impressed.

"Yes, that's what I told you the other day," Philip affirmed, his eyes scanning the well-presented paddocks leading to the farmhouse. "That was how he managed to get the job of building their sheep dip."

"And got you the job of painting the house for them," I added as the farmhouse came into view. "Looks lovely, Philip; well done." The footpath finished at the gravel road at the top of the Mount, which fed a hamlet of farmhouses, one of which was the home of John Owen, while immediately to our left was the wide metal gate leading to *Tŷ'n Gorse*.

We all huddled shyly behind Philip at the back door of the house, which was opened by an elegant lady who I suspected to be in her late fifties. Her carefully arranged shoulder-length black hair surrounded her attractive trim face, decorated with heavy but flattering blue eye makeup and rich ruby-red lipstick. She wore black stilettos and a tight-fitting calf-length black dress, which was split to the thigh, revealing slim legs clad in black fishnet stockings. The children were open-mouthed and speechless at her presentation, and I suddenly felt seriously underdressed and country bumpkin! However, Molly's lovely lips spread into a congenial smile, showing a sparkling set of white teeth as she warmly welcomed us into her home.

"Eeeee Philip, so this is your loovely family!" Molly said in a distinct Lancashire accent, taking us all into her loving gaze. "We've been looking forward to meeting you we 'ave; coom in," and she reached out and guided us into her cosy kitchen. "Would you like soom pop?" Molly asked, almost bending down to eye level with the children as they entered one by one into the room. Would they ever like some pop? They certainly would, they assured her, as she ushered them to the long kitchen table with its red and white chequered plastic tablecloth. There they sat in wide-eyed delight as Molly poured copious amounts of lemonade into their glasses and filled a large plate of biscuits for our hungry young travellers.

A small but effective coal-burning stove warmed the room and the shelves and windowsills were decorated with memorabilia and small vases of flowers. Precious children's drawings were attached randomly with blue tack to the walls, amongst pictures of fluffy baby animals that had been carefully cut out from glossy magazines by the young girl who was a daily visitor from a neighbouring farm. Despite her generous hospitality, I was beginning to feel rather concerned as I watched Molly gliding as graceful as a model between the fridge and the kitchen table.

"I'm sorry, we did not mean to disturb you," I ventured, "were you planning to go out somewhere?" Molly followed my gaze at her attire and laughed.

"Ooh noo Loove!" she replied, "I always dress oop at about six o'clock; it's force of 'abit at opening time from when we kept a poob up in the Moors," she reassured me. "We are always pleased to 'ave visitors." The other half of 'we' appeared at that moment from the depths of the house, wearing a red tartan open-necked shirt with braces to hold up his beige-coloured trousers. He was a well-built man, with a full, friendly face and kindly eyes under his heavy grey eyebrows. Dave was equally warm and welcoming, and it was evident that he was a well-cared-for and pampered husband. Molly beckoned him to join us at the table as she poured beers for the men and tea for me while she continued to ply the children with 'pop' and biscuits.

In my view, Molly looked every inch as though she could fit in perfectly as a barmaid, but nothing like my expectation of a farmer. Dave, on the other hand, could present very nicely as either stocky farmer or jovial bartender and my perception of him flitted between those roles throughout our first meeting and on into the warm and neighbourly relationship that was formed and cultivated between our two families.

15 Cestyll Gardens

"You will always find the best mussels where freshwater meets the seawater," Carl told Philip as they foraged amongst the rocks at the low tide line in the tiny, rugged bay of *Porth-y-Pistyll*, near Carl's home in Cemlyn. Daniel and Carl's son Jason thought it was a great game to be searching for those treasures with their fathers and quickly started filling their buckets with their collection. They were particularly fascinated to find some crabs of various colours and started to add them to their collection.

There were dark green-backed crabs and some with coral-tinted legs and lumpy chocolate-coloured backs. Some of the crabs they found looked exotic, displaying black and red stripes, but were quite aggressive. Carl and Philip were not too sure of the edibility of those crabs, so they recommended that the boys return them to the beach.

Oystercatchers piped in unison like quartets of piccolos as they swooped onto the water's edge and strutted along the shoreline, probing the mud with their long red, bladelike bills. They were rewarded with the discovery of bite-sized crabs and other tasty morsels uncovered by the receding tide.

A short distance away, Wylfa power station sat solidly atop the peninsular that jutted into the Irish Sea. The hum of its generators droned constant and monotonous over the bay. With his hair buffeted by the playful sea breeze, Philip stood and looked up at that controversial and dominating edifice and thought how out of place it looked in such a

Saffron

charming setting. He mused on the chance meeting he had with an elderly man just the weekend before.....

"Look at this!" My mother had proudly exclaimed when we turned up at my parents' home on that lovely, sunny Sunday. "We went for a nice fish and chip meal in the Harbour Hotel yesterday, and there it was on a rack just inside the door," she said, excitedly waving a colourful brochure in front of us. "Can you see who is on the front of it?" We all peered closely at the pamphlet she held, which displayed an attractive photograph of the Cemaes Bay harbour wall, taken during the RNLI regatta the previous summer.

"Oh, my goodness; it is you and Dad!" I exclaimed, and sure enough, on the front of the brochure, advertising the delights of Cemaes Bay were my parents leaning over the harbour wall. My mother was flushed with delight at her newfound fame, and our children regarded their grandparents with renewed respect.

Mum's delicious traditional Sunday lunch of roast beef with

all the trimmings of roasted potatoes, brussels sprouts, and boiled carrots, with a mountain of crisp and light Yorkshire puddings, filled with rich, dark brown meat gravy, was followed by apple pie and creamy custard. It never disappointed. After dinner, we rolled out on a slow walk around the bay while my Dad had his afternoon nap. On the way home, Philip and I left the children to continue down to the beach with their Nanny while we took a detour along the harbour wall.

All the world seemed to have come out of hiding on that delightful day at the beginning of May. It was a welcome taste of spring after the long months of winter, and a mostly wet and windy April. The tide washed soothingly into the harbour, where Philip's Drascombe Lugger rocked gently from side to side and the brightly coloured fishing boats, moored against the harbour wall, bobbed up and down with each shallow wave. Seagulls floated on the sheltered, blue-green waters in the hope of a meal of fish scraps from the fishermen. Fathers demonstrated to their offspring how to cast their fishing lines over the harbour wall while their mothers and the older members of the community sat and chatted happily on the benches that lined it.

Leaning over the wall and looking across the bay, we waved to my mother and watched as the children romped with her energetic black dog, Cassie. The tide was slowly lapping further in, narrowing the beach beside the Penrhyn Road, and on a cliff at the mouth of the bay sat Wylfa nuclear power station.

"Not a pretty sight!" Philip had said to the man who was also leaning over the wall beside us, and quietly looking in the same direction. The man turned toward us and smiled amiably.

"Excuse me?" he responded.

"The power station," Philip explained. "It is not a pretty sight amongst all this beauty, don't you think?" A sudden forceful breeze tried to whip off the man's trilby hat, which he pulled more firmly onto his head.

"I suppose that depends on whether or not your livelihood relies upon it," he replied, a smile creasing the corners of his eyes and spreading his well-groomed moustache widely across his aged cheeks.

'Not a local person,' Philip thought, as he studied the well-dressed man, 'possibly from the south of London from his accent.' The man turned back towards the view that he had been contemplating.

"Yes, many of the local community have been very grateful for employment in that power station," he stated sagely, and Philip felt somewhat chastened. "That station is a divider between the poor and the comfortable; people either love it or resent it. If you can get a job there you are made, and even the man who sweeps the floor is well-paid." The man spoke, not with passion, nor was he promoting any issue; he was merely stating a fact that we would find to be true over the coming years.

"It must be quite old now," Philip suggested.

"Yes," the man concurred. "The building started in 1963, and it became operational in 1971. I was there right at the beginning of the project as an atomic physicist and chief scientific officer; I retired in 1980 and decided to stay here in Cemaes." We were suddenly struck by the realisation that we were in the presence of an exceptional man and I could tell Philip was considering how to continue the conversation without voicing too much of an opinion.

"I appreciate that the project has been responsible and safety conscious; no 'Chernobyl' accidents, for example," Philip acknowledged tactfully. "But what I wonder is, when the station was built, was there a plan set in place for its decommission and projected costs at that time?" The man turned slowly toward Philip and graced him with that tolerant smile again; he studied Philip with a look of respect for asking such a perceptive question before returning his attention to the power station.

"You have to remember that the plans for this power station were formed not too long after the end of The Second World War," the man explained. "At that time, the development of nuclear energy had progressed very rapidly and had become employed in so many different situations. It was assumed that by the time Wylfa power station was ready to be decommissioned we would have learned how to deal with the problem cost-effectively." Philip was raptly attentive.

"And...have you?" he asked tentatively. The man took a deep breath and chewed pensively at his moustache.

"Sadly no, not yet," he replied. "That is why decommissioning has been postponed and the station has been granted permission to continue functioning for another ten years at least. After that, it could take decades, possibly even a hundred years until it would be completely safe. Who knows?" He turned his charming smile on us once more, touched the tip of his trilby politely and wished us a good day as he strolled in dignified fashion back toward the village.

'People either love it or resent it!' The words of that distinguished gentleman repeated themselves in Philip's thoughts as he stood on the beach of *Porth-y-Pistyll*, holding his bucket of mussels and looking at the proud object that had been under discussion on the previous Sunday. 'How will we feel about the power station in future years?' he wondered. Progressing along the beach, the team of fossickers came under the lee of a rocky hillside. As the fresh breeze dropped, an enticing aroma like the delicate scent of honey mingled with pine came wafting towards them. Philip stood up erect.

"What a delicious smell!" he declared. "Where is it coming from?" Everyone stopped what they were doing and looked around. That delightful fragrance filled the air and seemed to be coming from the direction of an ivy-swathed, disused water mill, which sat back from that isolated beach and just above the high tide line. Philip strode across a thick stone slab, serving as a bridge over the mill stream and headed toward the tumbledown building to investigate. He discovered a small gateway to its side, with a wrought-iron gate that had been wrenched from its hinges and was now lying on the ground.

"It's a garden, and it looks gorgeous!" Philip called out to the others.

"Aye, that will be Cestyll Gardens, Philip," Carl called back as he walked over to join him.

"Really? What is such a beautiful garden doing in a place like this?" Philip asked in surprise.

"It was planted by a Lady Violet Vivian about seventy years ago," Carl replied. "There was a grand old house here too."

"What happened to it?" Philip asked, intrigued. "Did it fall down?"

"The house is run down now, and I hear it is due to be demolished sometime soon," Carl answered, with a note of resentment in his voice. "The Lady sold the land on the condition that her garden should be cared for and open to the public."

"So, if it is open to the public, we can go in," Philip suggested enthusiastically, his horticultural passion aroused and the inviting aroma of spring flowers enticing him.

"It is only open on one miserly weekend a year though, Philip," Carl warned. "And this is just the back gate anyway."

"Well, it is open now," Philip grinned mischievously. "It looks like someone else disagrees with that once-a-year policy," he added, pointing to the discarded iron gate. "Are you coming?"

"I don't know," Carl answered, "I looked around it when it was open last year."

"Then you can give us a guided tour," Philip countered and reluctantly, Carl agreed, despite his misgivings. So, leaving their full buckets beside the gate, the foursome ventured cautiously through the little gateway into a 'fairy-tale world'.

The garden was nestled into a tiny natural valley between two steep-sided rock walls about twenty to thirty feet high. Although the sound of the wind could still be heard as it filtered through the protective shelterbelt of pine trees, the air in the garden was almost still, highly scented and even decidedly warm. The water mill was enshrouded by invasive but decorative ivy, which completely covered the mill wheel, leaving only a dark outline to mark its presence.

"*Gunnera Mantica*, or Elephant ears," Philip exclaimed, pointing to a broad, flat-leafed plant edging the melodious little stream that skipped daintily over the rocks, ran alongside the watermill, escaped across the beach and into the vast ocean. The stream was also flanked by ferns and mosses, New Zealand flax and Chatham Island Forget-me-nots, sweet-scented Viburnums and pale pink Daphne. Another thick slate slab served as a little bridge over the stream, where Fuchsias, in pinks and reds, hung low and daintily beside salmon-pink, orange and exquisitely perfumed golden-yellow Azaleas. Rhododendrons, in pink, white and red, were newly-opened and prolific. The fresh green of the Japanese maple, alongside the vibrant lemon-yellow of the Laburnum, stood in stark contrast to the mottled greens of the trees and bushes that formed the background. A small path of embedded flat rocks wove its way through the glade, leading to wooden bridges that crossed over the pretty, burbling stream, where large, orange Koi Carp twisted and turned vigorously. The team of explorers was wholly entranced!

Daniel excitedly related their wonderful day's experience at the kitchen table that evening while Philip stood at the sink preparing the bounty they had brought home. *Moules marinières* and homemade bread; it was a feast and all with so little cost.

"That was delicious!" Philip stated contentedly after the children had gone to bed. "But, given the proximity of that beach to the nuclear power station, I think it would not be wise to eat shellfish from there again; we just cannot be sure they are completely safe for consumption." A distant look washed over his face as he sipped his cup of tea.

"You know, I would quite like to work there in that little garden; maybe I will someday; we will have to wait and see."

16 Mellow May

The lambing madness was calming down as the month of May progressed, with just the odd expectant ewe still waiting to produce. Jill's four puppies had arrived safely; two black and white like their father and two red-brown and creamy-white like their mother. Despite being only a year old, she was a good mother and had settled quickly into her new role, emerging from her bed of hay in the old barn to join the family in the kitchen after leaving her little ones well fed and dozing contentedly.

A mellow dose of late spring warmth had settled over Mynydd Mechell; the sky was a vibrant blue with a defiant sun, which hovered bright and tardy to the north of Mynydd y Garn, even though it was after 8 pm. Pretty wildflowers had appeared in the verges and managed to stay awhile before being nibbled down by the sheep. Young leaves, pea green and translucent, fluttered playfully in the breeze on the sycamore trees lining the gorse-edged driveway while a

cascade of variegated green fields and hedgerows tumbled away decoratively toward Cemaes Bay.

Cemaes beach was our children's second playground after the farm. It is beautiful, even in the winter months, and as summer approaches, the old fishing village takes on vivid colours, enhanced by that special sea-side light. The little fishing port is fed by the *Afon Wygyr*, the river that flows from just below Parys Mountain to the sea at Cemaes harbour. It is joined along the way by the *Afon Meddanen*, the stream that drains *Llyn Llygeirian* and our reedy pool, *Llyn Bwch*. The arrival of holidaymakers brings exciting activity, which is why it was easy to understand the appeal of Cemaes Bay that had drawn my parents from the south of England to make it their home.

I watched that scene contentedly from my bed through the large, double-glazed window that our brother-in-law, PJ, had installed for us. What a difference the new windows made; these windows did not bow and rattle with the frequent attacks of ferocious windstorms at the change of seasons, so the house stayed warm and cosy. Life was good, the day's work was done, and the children were all fed and put to bed, so it was time for a luxurious, early night with sweet dreams.

At some point during my self-satisfied reverie, I became aware of a strange brown object that had loomed up from below the window and was wavering unsteadily just above the windowsill. After a few puzzling moments of watching that strange sight, I realised that it was a shepherd's crook and what was more, it looked as if it were about to crash against the window! I leapt out of bed and threw open the window just a second or two after the object noisily collided with its target.

There below was the culprit, still clutching the other end of the shepherd's crook and looking as though he was more shocked than I was. I was unsure if the look of alarm in his bright blue eyes was because he had almost smashed the window, or due to my shocking appearance with my face scrubbed and makeup-less and my hair all set in rags, ready for bed! He quickly composed himself, however, when he discovered that no harm was done, and a guilty smile broke out amongst his soft brown beard. His thick, unruly hair danced in the breeze while the end of his shirt collar drummed persistently on his face and a liberal dose of farm grime decorated his jumper and trousers. I remembered then why I had married him.

Then those romantic words I had heard so frequently in recent times floated up to my 'balcony' from my Romeo:

"Can you help me start the tractor?"

Oh, that tractor! What Philip could not do with it was yet to be listed. It came with a scythe mower, which was invaluable for cutting hay and clearing the Juncus rushes from the wetter areas of the farm. A set of chain harrows he had found buried amongst the undergrowth in the recesses of one of the fields proved very useful. That old-fashioned tool could be attached to the tractor and used to comb out the dead thatch from the grass sward, allowing new grass seed to germinate, thereby better utilising the light summer rains. Philip had collected several heaps of horse manure, free in exchange for cleaning out some riding school stables, and had dumped them in the field where he had found the chain harrows. He had devised an effective method of muck spreading, piling loads of manure on top of the chain harrows to give an even spread when dragged around the fields. At that time however, the tractor was essential for towing the trailer, loaded

131

with tools, sheep wire and fencing posts. Philip loved his new toy.

There was just one problem; it was almost impossible to start it running from cold. Unknown to Philip when he bought the tractor, this 1958 model had the four-cylinder Massey Ferguson engine, which we discovered was notoriously bad for starting. The starter motor did not have the power necessary to turn over the engine fast enough to make it fire into action. We had recently watched a documentary showing a tractor race between several Massey Ferguson 35s; before the race could begin, each tractor needed to tow the other to get them started. I told myself that if I ever met Ed Hillary in person, the first question I would ask would be: how on earth did he manage to make it to the South Pole in a Massey Ferguson 35 that always needed to be tow-started?

We decided that must have been the reason why John would not allow Philip to come up to his farm first thing in the morning to collect the tractor, preferring to drive it down to us later in the day, after it had been tow-started. Philip had tried using jump leads between the Volvo and the tractor, which just managed a miserable whining drone that progressively slowed to a grinding halt. Therefore, the tow-start method had been our daily ritual for the last few months since we had owned it, and then it was usually fine for the rest of the day, but not today. It was just as well that the vehicle we had bought to replace the microbus was a sturdy Volvo Estate with a towbar, which was far more suitable for our needs.

"But I'm all ready for bed," I protested weakly, knowing that protest was futile since there was no one else who could help and there was so much work to be done.

"It will only take a minute or two, and then you can get straight back to bed," Philip assured me, confident of my compliance and he went striding off to move the Volvo into position in front of the tractor. I heaved a heavy sigh and looked whimsically across the view that had been entrancing me before being brought back to the day's workforce. Skirting my bed, which was warm, inviting and vacant, I donned my dressing gown and tied a scarf over my ragged *coiffure*.

"You thought you were finished for the day, didn't you?" I quizzed my rubber boots, which lay in recumbent disarray outside the back door amongst all the others discarded by the family. I pulled them on and went to take my position in the driver's seat of the Volvo.

Having attached one end of the towrope to the towbar of the Volvo, Philip was lying on the grass, tying the other end to the axle at the front of the tractor. He seemed pleasantly surprised to see me already seated in the car when he looked up; his fencing equipment was all loaded into the trailer, and I could tell he was itching to get started.

"Right, let's go then!" Philip was up in the bucket seat of the tractor in an instant, fussing with various knobs and switches, and then a nod and a wave signalled that it was time to take off.

We made speedy progress down the lane with maximum acceleration, and we were almost at the farm gate when black smoke started to billow from the tractor's upright exhaust pipe. I stopped the car abruptly, but as I looked in my rear-view mirror, I noticed that Philip had not been quite as successful. The tractor was skidding and slewing in fascinating zigzag formation on the loose gravel driveway and heading rapidly toward the back of the car! It was very entertaining. Panic etched Philip's face as he wrestled with the steering wheel, and when he came to within a foot of the rear bumper of the Volvo, I thought it wise to edge forward a little, then he was finally able to bring his 'steed' to a halt. I watched as he pulled on the handbrake of the tractor, leapt swiftly from the seat and marched purposefully toward my open window. I thought I was in deep trouble!

"I nearly drove into the back of you!" he exclaimed as he leaned on the frame of the open car window.

"Oh, really?" I replied, checking my appearance in the mirror and tucking a random shred of rag back under my headscarf. Philip frowned at my raised eyebrows, and I was unsure if he believed in my innocence as he walked uncertainly back to release the towrope from the rear of the car.

"You know," Philip said thoughtfully when he came to bed a couple of hours later. "I parked the tractor on the top fields so I can roll it down the hill and jump-start it that way tomorrow. I might do that in future so you will not need to help me tow-start it every day. What do you think?"

"Good idea, Philip," I replied, satisfied with that outcome and I snuggled down contentedly between my white cotton sheets.

17 The Lawnmower

"Away! Come-Bye!" I was not sure who was training who in this sheepdog/shepherd relationship, but Philip was using commands such as he had heard Mr Davies using and Jill was a willing student, always keen to please her master whom she was learning to trust. She was an enthusiastic worker and, on the command, 'Over', she would gracefully jump over the nearest wall separating the paddocks so that she could round up the sheep. She was getting so proficient at this that one day she leapt over a four-foot-high wire fence, trapping her rear leg between the top two wires.

She yelped in terrible agony as she hung by her back leg and Philip dashed to her aid, taking her weight as he endeavoured to extract the leg from the twisted wires. Focusing on her excruciating pain, she was unable to work out that 'the boss is trying to help me'; all her instincts were to fight back, so she sank her teeth deeply into Philip's hands and arm.

Understanding that this behaviour was just a reaction to the pain, Philip continued to support her until he was able to free the leg, then he gently put her on the ground. She ran off with a noticeable limp about 30 or 40  yards, stopped for a moment as she thought things over, then turned around and came back, crouching low and submissively. With a slight wag of the tip of her tail, she licked Philip's wounds and face, doing everything possible to say, 'I am sorry, Boss' which was the cementing of their very close friendship. Under her master's direction, Jill soon became skilled at rounding up the flock and could move them from one field to another with speed and ease. They made a good team and gained the respect of most of the sheep, which quickly learned that being moved usually meant going to fresh pasture, so they were mostly eager and compliant.

It is not until you own sheep that you realise that each sheep has its own character and is not merely a wool-producing lawnmower. Philip got to know each of his sheep personally and our mealtime conversations about their antics could have made a good script for a TV series. However, we could not make out why one sweet little lamb was always in trouble. She would frequently be caught in the brambles, stumble into a ditch, or regularly find herself left behind when the flock was being moved. Her mother would run obediently with the rest of the sheep and then stand and call to her tardy offspring. After a few minutes, the little one would arrive, wrapped around the neck of her loving shepherd, who then placed his ward beside its mother. As I watched the way Philip handled her, I thought of the quotation on the front of the golden syrup tin that I read every week when I made a cake:

'Out of the strong comes forth sweetness.'

"It is probably blind," Arthur from *Pen Cae* confirmed Philip's suspicions. "Bracken!" stated Arthur astutely as he leaned on the metal field gate at the entrance to the flawless fields that surrounded his modest home. A halo of short, clipped, dark hair surrounded his shiny scalp and an old pipe protruded from amongst his neatly trimmed beard. "The mother probably ate bracken while she was pregnant," he nodded sagely to add emphasis to his diagnosis.

Philip knew that invasive weed needed to be controlled, as it was taking up a considerable amount of the best deep soil that should have supplied good grazing for the sheep. The bracken stems had cut deeply into his hands when he had tried to pull them by hand during his youth and he still bore the scars to remind him of the associated pain. Therefore, he was understandably reluctant to use such a method in dealing with the problem of bracken in our fields.

"So, what can I do about it?" Philip asked Arthur.

"Asulam," Arthur replied. Philip waited expectantly for some elaboration, but Arthur resumed chewing on his pipe as he leaned over his farm gate.

"Asulam?" Philip repeated.

"Not cheap; sixty pounds a gallon can," Arthur warned, removing his pipe from his mouth and examining its contents.

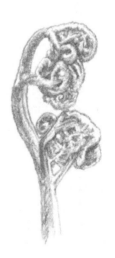

"Does it work?" Philip enquired.

"Not the first year," Arthur frowned, tapped his pipe on the gate to empty it of ash and he produced a spotless white handkerchief from the top pocket of his blue boiler suit to clean it. "Took three years to get rid of it on my place," he added, taking out a packet of tobacco from another pocket as he spoke and becoming absorbed in stuffing some of it into the bowl of his pipe. Philip thanked Arthur for his suggestion and left him to his pipe and his meditation. He knew he needed to do something radical to prevent the bracken from taking over the entire farm and possibly producing more blind sheep in future years. Sixty pounds for a product that may not be instantly effective sounded like a waste of money though; apart from that, he had disquieting thoughts about using herbicides. What was to be done?

The view across Bull Bay was stunning as we passed the Trecastle Hotel on our way to Paul and Candy's home at Pen Y Bonc, Amlwch the following Saturday. Philip had read in the newspaper about a Farm Closing Down auction, which was being held by their neighbours, so it made a good excuse for us to go to visit them. What was more, Paul had told us about a purchase that he had just made – a new lawnmower.

"What make is it?" Philip had asked on the telephone, but Paul was very secretive and suggested that we go to see it for ourselves.

The renovation work on their home, *Saith Môr,* had progressed well over the last year. Although self-taught, Paul had surprised us all, including himself, in demonstrating just what an accomplished DIY man he is. The sea view from their lounge window was spectacular and this formerly cold, un-inviting building was becoming a warm, charming and comfortable bungalow. The acre of land that they had bought with the house was mostly an overgrown tangle of gorse and brambles, into which he and Candy had been steadily carving a beautiful garden. As we drove into their driveway, we were met by two very excited dogs, named Jason and Holly, who bounded out of the house to greet us, closely followed by two equally excited children. Paul had been engrossed in planting some plants around the border of the new lawn that he had laid; he stood up to stretch his aching back and strolled toward us with a broad, welcoming smile.

"Come and see our new lawnmower!" Natasha and Hadleigh started toward the back of the house and beckoned our children to follow. Philip glanced at Paul with a look of bewilderment on his face, which said that a lawnmower was not exactly what town-bred children would generally consider high on their list of thrilling acquisitions. Paul just grinned, so we all followed the children to see the cause of the excitement.

"ME-ME-MERHHH!" stated the object of family delight; a little black and white Alpine goat kid! Her leather collar was tethered by a delicate chain to a metal stake in the ground amongst a host of 'scrumptious' vegetation. All the cousins were delighted with the 'new lawnmower'; we both laughed, and Philip gave Paul a dig in the ribs for tricking him.

"We just got her yesterday," Candy confirmed, as she appeared at the back door with some vegetable peelings for the newcomer. "We told the children they could come to help us choose a new lawnmower; they were totally disinterested until we drove onto the farm and they saw the herd of goats and their little kids. It was not a difficult choice to make, as this cheeky little thing came straight over and chose us."

Saffron

"Aaw! She is so cute!" I said, giving Candy a hug. "What have you decided to call her?"

"Lacy!" Natasha and Hadleigh sang out in unison. "Lacy-the-goat."

"ME-ME-MERHHH!" Lacy-the-goat concurred happily between mouthfuls of carrot peelings.

At the appointed time, Paul and Philip sauntered across to the farm where the auction was being held, while Candy, the children, and I took the dogs for a walk over the rugged clifftop. Jason was a handsome black mongrel and Holly, a lively, liver and white Springer Spaniel, who was so excited to be out walking that she barked the whole way.

Farm closing down auctions are often due to insolvency and are therefore usually sombre affairs, with the bidders feeling somewhat like 'vultures' cashing in on the sad predicament of the unfortunate farmer. However, this auction was a happy occasion since the farmer had recently made a very lucrative return on selling off a portion of his clifftop farmland for housing development and was now ready to retire and enjoy the profits.

Initially, Philip was quite disappointed; it seemed that there was nothing much of good quality for sale in the little field where the auction was to be held. There were two ageing tractors, a hay mower, a hay tedder for turning the cut hay, a hay baler and some battered-looking trailers, but none of them were in a well-maintained condition. Paul sifted through boxes containing assorted hand tools, various implements and general bric-a-brac. Philip started a perfunctory examination of one of the large cardboard boxes, which was full of near-empty plastic containers with faded, unreadable labels. Then something caught his eye; at the bottom of the box was an unopened gallon container of Asulam! Hoping that no one else had noticed his *serendipity*, Philip returned the unappealing containers on top of the Asulam and stood back amongst the bidders, where the man from Bob Parry Auctioneers was ready to start the auction.

"OK gentlemen!" the auctioneer began. "Let us start with these tractors............" The bidding was painfully slow, as it appeared that most of those present were waiting for the auctioning of the fields, so Philip guessed that he would not have much competition. The auctioneer steadily worked his way through the larger items, many of which were sold for a 'snip', and then it was on to the farm implements and smaller machinery. Eventually, attention was given to the boxes of bric-a-brac; Philip was tense as he watched the auctioneer's assistant lift the box containing the Asulam onto a plinth.

"Now we have here some boxes of fine agrochemicals," the auctioneer continued. "Let's start the bidding at ten pounds." There was silence amongst the bidders. Philip was feeling hopeful. "Five pounds; will anyone offer me five pounds?" A murmur of irritation rumbled amongst the crowd, Philip watched as some of them dug their hands into their pockets and shuffled their feet impatiently. "One pound?" the auctioneer looked expectantly around the gathering, but no one was interested. Philip decided this was his moment to strike!

"Fifty pence!" he called out, much to Paul's surprise. Some members of the crowd chortled derisively.

"Any advance on fifty pence?" The auctioneer scanned the assembly and then brought his hammer down swiftly on its block. "Sold for fifty pence!" he said and gestured for the next box to be put up on display. Paul looked at Philip as if he had gone mad!

"What did you want with that box of rubbish?" he asked in bewilderment.

"Ah, just you wait and see!" Philip replied with a self-satisfied smile. By the end of the auction, Paul had bid successfully for a Honda lawn mower (a real mechanical one this time), which cost him only £10 and was to be of excellent service to him for many years to come. Philip found himself the owner of a Lister sheep-shearing machine with the hand piece, which also cost £10, a set of disc harrows for £25, a high-quality, old-fashioned pitchfork with a sturdy ash wood shaft for £8 and a £60 container of Asulam herbicide for only fifty pence.

"You cunning fox!" Paul said with a grin when Philip told him why he had bid for the apparent 'box of rubbish'. They walked back to *Saith Môr*, happy and satisfied with their purchases, which would be delivered to the house later, to join their families for a welcome roast dinner.

"Lacy has escaped!" I blurted out as Paul and Philip rounded the corner and made to enter the driveway of *Saith Môr*.

"Oh, no!" Paul groaned. "How did that happen?"

"We just came back from walking the dogs along the cliffs, and when the children went out the back to check on her, she was gone," Candy explained as she came up behind me.

"Well, come on, let's spread out; we can all look for her," Philip suggested. "She won't be far away." Candy, Natasha and Amelia headed back along the clifftop with the dogs to check if Lacy had attempted to follow them. Philip and Daniel walked up the hill to see if she had decided to head for town, while Paul, Hadleigh and Joshua walked down to search the gardens at the lower end of *Pen Y Bonc*. I volunteered to sit out on the patio with my cup of tea, just in case Lacy turned up back at home. The search went on for about an hour, with various neighbours joining in the mission, however, she was nowhere to be found. Everyone looked stressed when they returned without her, with being Paul particularly upset about the situation.

"I think we should call the police, Paul," Candy recommended. "Maybe someone has found her and has reported her," she added hopefully.

"What a sad ending to a lovely day," I commented. "Shall I make a cup of tea for everyone, Candy?"

"Hey, Candy!" Paul's voice interrupted her reply. "Come and look at this!" The whole of the family search team followed Candy into the room to see what Paul had discovered. There in the middle of the lounge stood Lacy, watching the television while chewing on a succulent leaf from Candy's Swiss cheese plant.

"ME-ME-MERHHH!" Lacy-the-goat greeted the anxious assembly nonchalantly before returning her attention contentedly to her happy endeavour.

As Arthur had warned, the Asulam showed little immediate effect on the bracken during the first season of using it. What Philip did find to be instantly successful though, were the chain harrows he had discovered, hidden amongst the undergrowth in one of our fields. Trailing them along behind the tractor in the early summer, they would bend and damage the young crosiers of the bracken, without cutting them. Thus, the energy reserves in the starchy roots were diminished, progressively weakening that noxious pest while the Asulam gradually took effect.

We decided to call our little blind lamb 'Princess' and we attached a collar and bell to her mother so that Princess would know where she was in case she got herself lost. It was a daily event that the trusting little animal was brought home on Philip's shoulders, saved again from disaster and he still remembers the special feel and scent of her clean, white wool around his neck to this day.

18 Summertime Discoveries

"Philip! How are you?" Philip recognised his uncle's West Country accent instantly upon answering the telephone. "How would you like some Welsh Blacks?" We had not seen or heard from Uncle Alan since before our move to Wales the previous year, although Philip and Alan had always been firm friends, despite the distance between them. Alan ran a horticultural nursery in Taunton called Avery Nurseries, which he had developed into a thriving business. Since he was the much younger brother of Philip's mother, Alan was more like a cousin to him than an uncle.

"Why not? We don't have any black sheep," Philip responded after a few moments' consideration. "Maybe you could bring the boys up for a visit now that it is the school holidays. And how about bringing Toby and Sam with you; our Poppy is coming into season, and we would like her to have some pure Jack Russell pups."

Poppy did not appear to concur with that romantic invitation we noticed when the two amorous little dogs dropped eagerly from the van, which carried Alan, with his two boys, Adam and Martin, and the promised three black sheep. She hid coyly behind Philip, snapping and snarling at her suitors when they became too persistent, revealing a side of the normally quiet and mild little dog we had not seen before.

Alan has an effervescent personality with a likeable dose of mischief. With his cheeky smile and a tousled thatch of straw-coloured hair, we found him to be an entertaining visitor, while his boys were good company for our children. Philip and Alan chatted enthusiastically as they and the children explored the smallholding, along with Jill and Poppy, followed by her ever-present, ardent entourage.

"Your sheep are looking good, Philip," Alan commented as we

adults sat together at the kitchen table drinking tea after a good lunch while the children went back to play in the fields. "You have not given in to the trend to feed them this meat and bone meal product on the market then?"

"What?" Philip shot his uncle a shocked expression. "Who in their right mind would feed meat to vegetarian animals?"

"Not me, for sure!" Alan assured him, "but it is becoming quite popular; you must be out of touch if you have not heard about it."

"That's disgusting! It's the first I have heard about it," Philip was revolted by that piece of information.

"Yes, I thought you would feel the same as me," Alan nodded. "I can see no good coming of it."

"I cannot believe the Ministry of Agriculture would allow this to happen," Philip exclaimed, scratching his head and frowning at the thought. "This is surely going to turn around and bite them in the rear!" A sense of foreboding hung heavily in the kitchen that day, although none of us was then aware that the first cases of bovine spongiform encephalopathy, or BSE had recently been discovered in the United Kingdom. It was diagnosed as a neurodegenerative disorder and, as we feared, was linked to feeding cattle with infected meat and bone meal products. Within a short time, the devastating effects of that disease, commonly known as 'mad cow disease' swept the country, leading to the slaughter of millions of cattle in an attempt to stop its spread. Sadly, other animals and even some humans who had unwittingly consumed infected beef products became seriously ill. British beef was banned from export, bringing Britain's meat industry to its knees.

That summer however, the impending agricultural 'storm' that threatened the country was obscured by the tranquillity of our surroundings and we were keen to show Alan and the boys the delightful discoveries we had made over the past months. We took them on our favourite walks to the beaches of Cemaes Bay,

146

around the clifftops to *Porth Padrig*, or White Lady Beach. A large sea stack made of hard white quartz stands solidly in the middle of the beach, locally known as the 'White Lady', after *Ladi Wen*, a 'ghost' from Celtic mythology.

En route, we spent some time amongst the gravestones behind Llanbadrig church, reading the names of those interred who had lived such short lives hundreds of years earlier. According to the sign on the church door, we were standing on one of the oldest Christian sites in Britain, dating back to AD 440. Legend has it that the church was founded by and named after St. Patrick when he survived a shipwreck on *Ynys Badrig*, an island locally known as Middle Mouse. We gazed out at the stretch of sea, which would have crashed fiercely against that rocky island during stormy weather, and we thought of the tragedies of those lost in shipwrecks to those wickedly treacherous waters.

"Do you think the boys would like to visit a pottery tomorrow, Alan?" I suggested, after enjoying a great pub lunch at the Harbour Hotel in Cemaes. "One of our friends recommended Piggery Pottery, a little studio in Llanberis, where the children can make their own pots and paint them; we have been meaning to visit there for some time now."

"Aprons on, boys," the cheerful, sunny lady commanded as she prepared Adam and Martin before establishing them on a couple of tall stools behind their potters' wheels. Alan's boys were keen to test their skill, while the rest of us stood at a safe distance, cheering them on encouragingly. It looked rather daunting to our children so they chose some ready-made character lamps to paint at home.

Is it not amusing to watch children as they attempt to perform arts and crafts while their doting parents look on? Adam and Martin beamed broad smiles at their audience from under their white-blond fringes while the lady helped them to cup their hands around the lumps of moist clay set on the wheels. Copious amounts of water were poured over the clay as the wheels started to turn and the boys' faces became alive with the delight of being in control. Well, how much they were 'in control' was a matter of opinion. As the aspiring pots grew taller, they started to wobble. That is the turning pots stayed in place, but the boys wobbled with enormous smiles on their rapt faces, never once taking their eyes off their father, who was trying his level best to control his laughter. They did not need to say, "Watch me, Dad!" their eyes said it all.

"Oh, well-done, boys. I think that is enough now," one of the ladies overseeing those 'works of art' declared, as she switched off the power and assisted her wards to climb off their stools. The contorted versions of *The Leaning Tower of Llanberis* were sliced skilfully off their wheels with a wire and then left to dry until they were ready to be kiln-fired and later sent to them by post. We all trooped into the little café area for some refreshments.

"How about a picnic on the beach tomorrow?" Philip suggested over tea and scones.

"Ah, you would love that, wouldn't you, boys? Where do you recommend?" Alan asked. Philip and I looked at each other and instantly agreed on the perfect beach: Lligwy, near Moelfre.

We thought it would be informative to visit the RNLI lifeboat station at Moelfre before moving on to the beach the following day, and it was certainly an education. The bravery of those lifeboat volunteers is humbling, especially when called out to an emergency during a fierce and terrifying storm coming down from the north! While there, we learned about one of the worst tragedies known to the area.

A steam clipper called, The Royal Charter was returning from Australia during the Gold Rush with a stash of gold in the hold and had foundered on the rocks just north of Moelfre in 1859. Sadly, about four hundred and fifty passengers and crew were lost in that shipwreck after having travelled so far.

"This certainly is a dangerous coast!" Alan observed, moved by the information presented at the station. Having seen that sea in all its raging winter fury, we had to agree.

"Come on," Philip said in an effort to lighten our spirits. "I want you to see something before we have our picnic." Parking our vehicles in a pretty country lane, lined with hawthorn and sycamore hedgerows, quite close to Moelfre, we passed through a small gate and followed the marked footpath. Eventually, we reached some fascinating ancient earthworks; partly bordered by mature ash trees was the excavated and well-preserved Iron Age village of *Din Lligwy*. As we stood looking with amazement at the village previously buried beneath hundreds of years of history, we found it hard to comprehend its antiquity. The lichen-covered limestone village walls were four to five feet thick and formed an irregular-shaped pentagon, while remnants of circular and rectangular buildings flanked the insides of the walls. We thought of what a money-making enterprise it would have been if found in the south of England, but here, with no ticket office and no 'Private, Keep Out' signs, anyone could explore the site and absorb its atmosphere at any time and without charge.

The children pretended to be villagers, each claiming one of the buildings as their own personal 'home'. Amelia stirred an imaginary pot of soup over her make-believe fire while Joshua and Martin came to visit for lunch with their imaginary bowls and spoons.

"I think they are getting hungry," I commented. So we decided to pick up some chips to take to our destination of Lligwy Beach. The day was delightfully warm and sunny, and the sea washed in and out, clean, clear and sapphire blue, creating rippled patterns across the sandy beach. It was a perfect day for swimming and taking turns in Alan's kayak, while the dogs splashed happily in the water, bounding along the beach as though it was the best day of the summer.

It was sad to say goodbye to Alan, Adam and Martin at the end of the week as the lively group waved farewell and disappeared down the lane. However, we had made the most of every day together; we had explored the Island and beyond, renewed friendships, gained three black sheep and, as we were soon to discover, a litter of Jack Russell puppies.

19 The Mills of Llandeusant

August was a beautiful month, and our children spent a lot of time outside doing Nature studies, often accompanied by two dogs, an assortment of chickens and a group of bottle-fed lambs that were now weaned but still considered themselves part of the family. Jill's puppies had all found good homes; my Mum had chosen one that resembled Jill and named her puppy, Lucy. Dozy Nora's twins, which were evidently fathered by a Suffolk ram, were growing quite large and robust, and Dora would often 'mug' the children when they were sent down to the lower field with the boiled potato peelings to feed the chickens. Poor Amelia appeared at the back door one day with the empty bowl in her hand and mud all over her face, having been 'attacked' from behind and flattened, face down in the field. We decided it was best to leave that job to Philip in the future.

One evening, while the children were splashing about in the bath with their ducks, boats and bubbles, Mr Davies' truck pulled up in the driveway. Jill recognized the sound of the vehicle, and bounded over to greet her boyfriend, Tweed, as he leapt excitedly from the cab. Mr Davies was always a welcome visitor, so Philip invited him inside and offered him a *panad.*

"Just a moment, I have a small gift for the children," Mr Davies replied. He walked back to his truck, returning with the most adorable little lamb nestled in his arms. "She is the last of the flock to be born," he explained. "I need to get her fully weaned so her mother can get into good breeding condition before being put to the *tup.*"

"Oh, she is beautiful!" we all exclaimed when Philip carried her into the bathroom to show the children. She was the cutest little lamb we had yet seen; clean, round, fluffy-white and not much bigger than a teddy bear. Amelia held out her arms, so Philip carefully placed the docile little creature into them; the next thing we knew she was in the bath as well! I am sure it was not what Philip had in mind and probably not recommended, but there she was, all bubbled up, having her shampoo session, and it was too late to object.

"How kind of Mr Davies," I pointed out to remind the children of their manners.

"Thank you, Mr Davies," they called out in unison.

"And what do you think you will name her?" I asked.

"Beauty!" Joshua declared decisively, and all agreed.

During that visit, Philip asked Mr Davies about dog food as Jill was not responding well to the tinned food we had been feeding her. Thus we were introduced to the mills of Llanddeusant.

'*Melin Llynnon* is the last working windmill still operating in North Wales. Built in 1775-1776 and renovated in 1984, it attracts visitors from all over the world to watch its enormous white sails turn with powerful grace by the strength of the Anglesey winds.'

As we stood on the pathway before that regal, whitewashed edifice, attempting to read the related brochure, despite the wind trying to wrench it from our hands, we found the windmill to be just as described. Small windows were set into its towering white façade with a little door at its base, while its massive sails creaked and billowed with mesmeric elegance as they turned with the power of the forceful wind. We thought of the changes that mill had seen in its centuries of employment and the generations of hard working millers that had fed the populace by means of it. And it was still doing a good job in the 1980s.

However, it was the nearby watermill, *Melin Hywel*, which would change our habits and lifestyle. That attractive stone-built mill with its small windows, low slate roof, and enormous millstones propped against its ancient walls was still in working order, and we thought it quite charming.

A small flock of ducks chattered happily on its emerald green millpond, fed by a diversion from the *Afon Alaw,* which cascaded prettily over the steadily turning mill wheel, and then danced away 'liberated' between the wooded banks. The miller was happy to show us around inside the mill, explaining how each piece of machinery worked and how the granite millstones ground the grain, fine, medium, or coarse The processed grain dropped down

to the basement and into hessian sacks where, using the power of the waterwheel, a hoist in the loft lifted them up through the trap doors, passing the grinding floor, then further up to the storeroom on the top floor. They then went to local bakers as 56-pound, sewn paper sacks of traditional stone-ground, whole-grain or white flour. The price was very reasonable, so we bought one sack of each. The watermill also supplied Pero™, a dog food specially made from dried meat and cereal, which Mr Davies had recommended as a far healthier diet for our dogs, and which we found suited them very well.

The lady at the bakery in Cemaes Bay was a jolly sort of person with a round, smiling face that was framed by grey curly hair. She regularly reserved us a two-pound block of fresh yeast for just £1, which handled like a lump of grey plasticine, taking me back to the delights of childhood play. A small knob added to the warm sugar water quickly melted and bubbled rewardingly. The combination of the velvety flour, raised slowly with the fresh yeast broth and then baked in the Rayburn was a sure recipe for success. Monday soon became bread-baking day; I would knead eighteen pounds of flour in a sizeable new plastic dustbin until I was too heavy with child, and then Philip would continue the routine.

One day, my sister Candy was alarmed to see that our little fridge held only a bottle of milk and a block of yeast. To me that fridge held a potential colourful feast, and I was keen to experiment with whatever could be made with flour and yeast. I learned to make bread rolls, pizza bases, lardy cakes, and currant buns covered in pink or white icing, which Joshua named 'bumper cars'. It was amusing how many friends started calling in as they 'just happened to be passing' our remote location on a Monday baking day. The freezer was filled at the end of the day with whatever was left over, which would keep us well fed until the next baking day, a week later.

Nettle Ginger beer became a popular beverage with the children, made with boiled nettle tips, a little yeast, powdered ginger, sugar and lemons. Daniel officiated as chief drinks server, scooping the delicious nectar from a large barrel beside the table at mealtimes. It kept the children healthy and happy, and if they started getting giggly, we knew it was time to top up the brew with more water.

Running through the fields with their friends and cousins who came to visit, they laughed, played and explored all the wonders of the countryside. They dragged mountains of sand through their grandparents' seaside home as we spent many summer days on the beach at Cemaes Bay. We would often finish the long days by eating my mother's delicious home bakes while those who were permitted savoured her home brews. Thus, the summer passed happily, and Poppy and I sympathized with each other as we both grew larger with offspring.

As the sun descended on those lovely summer evenings, we formed a family tradition of gathering together from wherever we happened to be to sit on a wide, flat, rocky ledge in the top fields of the farm. There we would watch as the sun slid along the shimmering waters of Cemlyn Bay, silhouetting the imposing form of Wylfa power station, before dipping below the horizon and into the Irish Sea. At the height of summer, the light did not disappear completely, but a gentle glow lingered in the northern sky, and then, by the very early hours of the next morning, the sun was already climbing up again on its new day's circuit.

Sand Pies

By Nanny Doreen

Sand pies stand on Granddad's lawn
Spades and buckets so forlorn
Dropped in play when called for tea
"Not just yet," we hear the plea.

The garden's empty, the line is bare
The chatter's stopped, the hall is clear
Of shoes and coats and toys and bags,
Of shells and stones and empty crabs

Upstairs the bathroom's clean and bright,
Not a soggy towel in sight.
The toothpaste cap is still in place
Not one puddle can we trace.

The sheets are changed off empty beds
Pillows once dented by curly heads
Ready again for their return,
Their journey home was our concern

That elusive sock was under the bed;
The works of art in crayon red
Adorn the fridge for all to see
"We love you, Nanny".....just for me.

The driveway no longer a "Car Sales site,"
The cars have gone, have put to flight.
We drive in and out with such ease;
We only have ourselves to please.

The best of both worlds is what we love,
The peace and quiet and the noisy hub.
Of hectic holidays with family and seed
Just a breath in between is all that we need.

20 October Arrivals

Tupping season had started at the end of August for many of the local Suffolk sheep farmers who wanted their ewes to be among the first to produce in early January. The aim was to get the highest prices for their lambs, which would be ready for the butcher by late spring. However, we had already experienced one Anglesey winter, and Philip did not relish lambing again in the brutal winter chill. Therefore, as Mr Davies advised, we had delayed putting the rams in with the ewes until mid-September so the lambs would be born in the spring.

Nero, the stocky Welsh Mountain ram with his exaggerated Roman nose and regal spiralled horns, and his enthusiastic companion Gus, the leggy Beulah, had been rounded up into the small pen by the barn. Philip then attached their raddle harnesses with bright red wax blocks on the underside of their chests, which would leave a mark on the backs of the ewes they covered. He was to change the colour of the wax blocks every two weeks to identify which ewes would be the next to give birth. Daniel, Amelia and Joshua watched the subsequent activities with curiosity, and it was an informative introduction to the 'Facts of Life'.

During that first year of living in Mynydd Mechell, we discovered that there seemed to be a particular protocol attached to first meetings: What is the family name? What is the name of your house? What does your husband do for work? Which church do you attend? Church/Chapel/other? Where do your children go to school? 'Home-schooled' was evidently not a suitable option, as it was usually at this point that the smiles disappeared, and the conversation was rapidly concluded.

It was apparent that Education, along with Cleanliness, of course, was next to Godliness. Therefore, since Daniel and Amelia had started attending the English school in Cemaes Bay at the start of the new school term, we were becoming more acceptable members of the community. Also, children are excellent ice-breakers, especially when they spend their pocket money in the Post Office shop on sweets or *pethau da*. The Post Office was quite the hub of village society, so it was there that everyone gathered to learn the local gossip. Mrs Jones was a very helpful postmistress, always happy to teach me new words in Welsh if the Post Office was not too busy.

One day, however, the Post Office was bristling with excited villagers and spirited conversation. Word had gone around that a film company had sent out some scouts to find the best location to shoot a new movie, and they were considering Llanfechell.

"Well, why not?" Mrs Hughes regaled Mrs Williams in her appealing Welsh accent as they waited in the Post Office queue. "They must be impressed with the countryside around here," she continued, turning to Mrs Owen, whose husband ran the local garage. Mrs Owen was watching out through the Post Office window.

"Oh, look!" Mrs Owen's tone alerted the ladies to some activity going on outside. "They are taking photographs of the War Memorial," she chirruped excitedly. "And they are taking photos of your cottage, Mrs Pritchard." Everyone collected in a cluster of woollen coats and bobbing headscarves at the window, leaving Mrs Jones partway through handing Mrs Pritchard the book of stamps she had just bought. Mrs Pritchard wished she had cleaned the box sash windows on her cottage yesterday when she had washed the lace cotton curtains. Still, the weather had suddenly turned quite cold and windy, which, as we had discovered the year before, was typical of October and certainly not the sort of days for cleaning windows.

'*Dim ots*,' she thought, trying to convince herself that it did not matter as she watched the progress of the photographers. 'All the other windows in that row of cottages could have done with a good clean too, except for those of Mrs Lewis who cleaned her windows at least once a week.'

The ladies watched in fascination as the well-wrapped scouts moved across from behind the War Memorial and started taking photos of the old church, seeming particularly interested in a marble statue inside the churchyard. However, the wind on that corner was making it difficult to hold their cameras steady, and a sudden gust sent one or two scouts chasing after a sheaf of papers, which whirled and scattered coquettishly across the little village square. The camera men then swung around to take photographs of the Post Office, where a sudden scramble and colliding of shopping baskets ensued as the spectators returned rapidly to its depths. Mrs Jones, who had remained behind the Post Office counter, was mesmerised by the proceedings and was still holding Mrs Pritchard's book of stamps in mid-air. The villagers were modest people who, although always curious about anyone or anything new, were too well-mannered to appear nosey.

Apparently, the movie scouts were looking for a setting suitable to tell the tale of a couple who met in Ireland and were continuing their romance in an obscure village in the most inhospitable, cold, grey depths of Russia. Unaware of that at the time, the people of Llanfechell were overwhelmingly proud that their village was the one chosen as ideal for the part!

A village committee meeting was held in the local school soon after the departure of the movie scouts and decided that the village of Llanfechell was long overdue some care and attention. Mrs Jones was relating to the small group gathered at the Post Office, the events of the meeting that had been held the evening before in Llanfechell school hall and had politely broken into English as Joshua and I entered after dropping Daniel and Amelia at school.

"'Being the main tourist attraction of the region Cemaes Bay has had priority on Council grants for house renovations,'" Mrs Jones repeated the words of the council officer, Alwyn Jones from Llangefni, who had been there to officiate at the meeting. He had a good point, Mrs Jones' audience agreed, nodding and muttering amongst themselves.

"'Tregele does not need much council restoration work done, but Mynydd Mechell needs consideration,'" Mrs. Jones continued to relate the comments of Alwyn Jones. "That would be good news for you, Mrs Barlow," Mrs Jones acknowledged, nodding and smiling benevolently at me as I was encouraged to seat myself on a rickety wooden chair by the counter. As I was nearing the end of my pregnancy, I was treated with the utmost consideration when I called in to cash my Family Allowance cheque.

Four-year-old Joshua, with his big blue eyes and heavy blond fringe, was charming the ladies as usual, who started plying him with biscuits bought from the shop. Mrs Jones then drew herself up to her full height and looked down her nose in emulation of the authoritative air of Mr Alwyn Jones.

"'We may not have the funds to address the needs of Llanfechell at the moment,'" she repeated his words in as manly a mode as she could muster. "'But certainly, after the other villages have been renovated, possibly within the next five years, we will consider when we can start work on Llanfechell.'" Mr Alwyn Jones may have been confident that his report would be satisfactory, but the local villagers were not at all appeased. I could tell that from the emphatic way Mrs Jones stamped the stub of my Family Allowance book.

Thwack! I flinched, and the baby inside me jumped in surprise and began to kick. However, Mrs Jones was proud to announce that her cousin, Mr Ifor Morgan, a very sage and sensitive man in his late sixties, had taken it upon himself to speak on behalf of the disgruntled representatives of the people of Llanfechell:

"'Respectfully, Mr Jones, we do have a bit of an emergency here in Llanfechell,'" he had reportedly said. Other attendees at that committee meeting then began to voice their objections to that decision, which Mrs Jones now animatedly repeated. To the delight of Mrs Jones' Post Office audience, Ifor Morgan had invited his good friend, Aled Gwyn to the meeting, who had been born in Llanfechell and was now a government official in the Welsh Development Agency in Cardiff. Mr Gwyn had countered the statement of Mr Alwyn Jones with the welcome news that European Community funds were, in fact, available for the refurbishment of Welsh villages and, in view of the pressing need to present Llanfechell village suitably for the film company, the work could start almost immediately!

Thwack! Mrs Jones stamped the back of my cheque triumphantly and counted out my money.

Lynnette

"Buttercup! Buttercup Barlow." Robert Black was amused by his own suggestion when he and his wife Katherine tried to guess the name of our new baby girl.

"It is yellow and grows in the fields," Candy had given them that clue when she greeted them and their little ones, Rebecca and baby Joseph, at our kitchen door, and she kept them guessing all the way up the stairs.

"Primrose? Crocus?" offered Katherine.

"Close!" Candy replied.

"Tulip? Laburnum?" It was evident that this little family were amongst our friends who came from the south of England, where there was a greater variety of garden flowers to choose from that did not need to struggle against the ravages of the Anglesey winds.

"Daffodil!" Little Rebecca contributed.

"Hypericum?" The suggestions were becoming more exotic and unlikely as our visitors trailed along the passageway until they all peered around the doorway.

Candy's children, Natasha and Hadleigh, were playing on the bedroom floor with our children and Natasha and Amelia leapt up and ran to the bedroom door at the sound of their little friend's voice.

"Saffron!" the children sang out in chorus as the family presented me with a lovely bouquet and gathered around our little sleeping beauty in her crib. We had settled on the name 'Amber', but when we saw her, we felt that she did not suit that name. Candy had been very pleased when Philip agreed that our little new-born, with her big, blue, dewy eyes, looked the perfect 'Saffron', the name she and Paul would have chosen had Hadleigh been a girl. Yes, Saffron, that very precious deep yellow spice, made from the stamens of the crocus, we explained, and we all quickly came to love both the name and the child.

Two days later, Poppy produced four tiny and adorable tricolour puppies. Her cuddly little offspring with their soft white coats and black and tan patches snuggled comfortably, suckling contentedly on her abundant milk supply when I visited her in her cosy bed in the old barn.

"Well done, Poppy!" I congratulated. "It took you only nine weeks to accomplish what it took me NINE YEARS to achieve!"

21 Lamb Chops

Joshua missed the company of his older brother and sister since they had started school; although he could have started school at the same time, we had decided to keep him back until after the winter holidays. We wanted to make sure he did not feel pushed out and replaced by his new little sister since he had been the baby of the family for four and a half years.

Along with Jill the sheepdog, Joshua had been Philip's constant companion, and during the autumn his little blackberry-stained hands and face told of the fun he had while helping with the work to be done. Following behind his Daddy with the wooden nail box they had made together, he carried staples in one section and four-inch nails in the other, ready for work on the remaining fencing. Philip taught Joshua the importance of hitting a nail straight, and then he would finish off Joshua's efforts to make him feel like a successful part of the team, teaching him skills that would set him in good stead for his future career.

Philip took the time to teach his little helper the names of the animals, trees, plants, and birds as they worked together, forming a special close bond between them. One day, while attaching sheep mesh to a fence post, Philip leapt back with a cry of surprise! He came face to face with a pine marten, the size of a large feline, which poked its head out

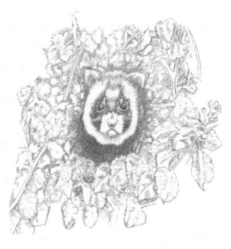

from among an ivy-clad hawthorn! Man and beast were equally shocked by the encounter, and Joshua found it all very amusing.

Shortly after the arrival of Saffron, we decided it was time to sell the lambs of the season. They had been weaned off their mother's milk by then, and the very distressing few weeks of hearing the lambs and their mothers calling pitifully to each other from their separate fields had eased up as they all became accustomed to their new situation. However, apart from the fact that we had grown fond of our lambs and were sad to have to sell them for meat, Philip had another concern.

"I don't suppose we will get very much for the lambs," he commented as we watched them through the kitchen window. "Most other farmers will have raised their lambs on far better pasture than we have had here, so there will be a lot more fat on them."

"Does it matter?" I asked while washing up the breakfast dishes.

"Well, yes, of course," Philip countered. "Everyone knows that fat lambs mean they have been raised on the best grass, don't they?"

"Maybe you are thinking more about our reputation as farmers, Philip," I suggested after a few moments of contemplation. "But what does the housewife look for when she goes to the shop to buy meat for the family? I would always search out the leanest of cuts so as not to waste any of it." Philip rubbed at his beard as he continued to watch the lambs grazing contentedly.

"Do you think that could be our speciality then, 'lean meat' production?" he suggested, his face lightening at the thought. "Rather than sending them to the market as live lambs, perhaps we should sell them as butchered lambs?"

"Why not?" I replied.

John Owen recommended a very proficient butcher who had a

respectful and humane approach to his trade, and we quickly found customers for our first batch of butchered lambs from amongst our friends and neighbours. Word spread fast that the meat was delicious, possibly because the lambs' diet contained so many species of wild herbs. I found it painful to watch all the lambs go off in the trailer, knowing they would be returning two days later in large plastic bags. However, I had to admit that being a 'townie', that was how I had always been used to having my meat presented. Anyway, my ethics soon melted with the tantalising smell of lean lamb, roasting in the Rayburn's oven and its succulent flavour as it blended with roasted potatoes, honey roasted carrots, mint sauce and Yorkshire puddings, covered in rich meaty gravy.

"This looks interesting!" Philip was drinking his mid-morning coffee at the kitchen table and sifting through the local newspaper he had picked up after dropping the children at school.

"Wanted! Qualified lambing assistant, local to Llanbabo," he read aloud, circling the advertisement in red biro. "That's just over the hill from us; I could do this!" I leaned over his shoulder to look at the job advertisement as I rocked baby Saffron to sleep in her coach pram under the kitchen window. It was our second January living at *Tŷn Llain,* and we were enjoying the routine and cosiness of the place. Philip had finished the fencing, and most of the sheep were pregnant. Joshua had started school with Daniel and Amelia in Cemaes Bay as planned after the winter holiday, and they all seemed happy with their new friends and with what they were learning.

Philip did not like to be idle, so he was ready for a new project; apart from that, we were draining the last of our savings and needed to earn some money. The sale of butchered lambs brought us a welcome return, but it was nowhere near enough to meet our annual needs. John Owen and Leslie had warned us that work for 'outsiders' was scarce, and the local people did not have the funds to employ a landscape gardener. Despite being an experienced horticultural worker, Philip was offered a job working for a landscaping company for the miserly wage of fifteen pounds a day, which was well below the legal minimum wage. The employer had a team of about six men already working for him.

"How do they manage to live on just fifteen pounds a day?" Philip asked.

"Ah, well, they all have 'other income'," their boss replied with a knowing wink, which Philip clearly understood to mean that they were also drawing government unemployment benefits.

"Well, I would not do that!" Philip was very irritated by the man's reply. "So, thanks, but no thanks!" he said and took his leave.

"Will you have some tea with us, Mr Barlow?" The gently spoken farmer's wife had sat Philip at the kitchen table while they waited for her husband to come in from the fields. Llanbabo was the neighbouring hamlet to the southeast of Mynydd Mechell, where the pastures looked lush, green and with very little gorse. The soil was evidently deeper and more fertile and, as it was south-facing, had longer sunshine hours than on our side of the mountain.

Bevan Williams joined Philip at the table after scrubbing his hands at the kitchen sink and winced as Philip shook his hand firmly and enthusiastically.

"I can tell you are a hard worker," Mr Williams commented, gesturing at the size of Philip's strong hands.

Mrs Williams placed plates of lamb chops in front of the two men and returned from the Aga cooker with a pan of steaming vegetables, which she distributed between them and covered liberally with thick, rich gravy. Philip was surprised since he was only expecting a cup of tea, not a full meal!

"So, what makes you feel qualified for this job?" Mr Williams asked as he filled his mouth with a whole boiled potato. With Mrs Williams watching him from the far side of the kitchen, Philip attempted to answer politely and convincingly while doing his best to look as if he was hungry and enjoying that delicious meal since he had already eaten at home before the interview.

'This is not the ordinary job interview,' he thought.

"Well, I did a lambing course last January, and I managed the lambing for my own flock," Philip answered, wiping gravy from his chin with the well-pressed cotton napkin Mrs Williams had provided.

"So, you keep sheep then, Mr Barlow?" Mr Williams asked, picking up a lamb chop and devouring it with relish. Philip was quite relieved that this was acceptable and followed suit. Mrs Williams smiled indulgently from the kitchen as she wielded a tea towel and watched his every mouthful, taking pleasure in the men doing justice to her cooking.

"Yes, but I won't start lambing until after your lambing finishes," Philip assured. Mr Williams eagerly accepted 'seconds', while Philip sensed Mrs Williams' disappointment at his polite refusal, having struggled to do justice to 'firsts'.

"Hmm…. I am not so sure about the size of your hands, though," Mr Williams frowned as he noticed how the knife and fork seemed decidedly minuscule enveloped in Philip's large, work-roughened hands. "How did you get on with the lambing last year?" he asked pointedly.

"Oh, I got on fine!" Philip answered, smiling nervously. However, the look on Mr Williams' face contorted into a sympathetic grimace, indicating his misgivings on whether our poor ewes would agree with that statement.

"Perhaps your wife should go on the lambing course," he recommended, and Philip rightly concluded that he would not be chosen for the job.

Whether it was due to his large hands or because he did not show adequate gusto for Mrs Williams' delicious meal, Philip did not hear back from Mr Williams about the job. However, he had learned a lot about the local customs of warm hospitality. Moreover, it was decided, by popular opinion, that it was time for me to go on the lambing course.

22 Starburst

"Don't worry. Don't worry. You will be OK!" Philip said, attempting to soothe the next ewe to be scanned, holding her between his knees before manoeuvring her into the tubular steel cradle that Sally the vet had brought up to the farm. With the push of a lever, the cradle gently lifted the ewe, turning her onto her back. Sally smeared a clear gel over its tummy before carefully running the hand-held scanner across it.

"This is a single lamb," she said, pointing to the faint image on the screen beside her. Philip picked up one of the stock markers and sprayed a blue mark on the ewe's side. Sally Owen was an amiable lady, the wife of the local doctor, and Philip had met her two weeks earlier when he and Daniel had gone to help Dave and Molly with the scanning of their ewes. She had such a pleasant way with the animals she treated and commented on Philip's tender interaction with his sheep.

"Now, this next one is called Jemima," Philip said as he fondly rubbed the rust-coloured forehead of his favourite sheep. "Jemima is the free one we were given, and she is a real good 'un, aren't you, Jemima?"

"Do you always talk to your sheep like that?" Sally asked as she identified twins for Jemima.

"Yes, I do; it puts them at ease," Philip replied, selecting the red stock marker and spraying a mark on Jemima's side. "Well done, Jemima!" he said proudly, holding out a handful of sheep nuts for her, as he had done with all the other sheep who had submitted to the scan that morning.

"Jemima is having twins, Lynnette!" Philip announced when I brought out mugs of tea to the little sheep-pen where they were working to warm them against the cold day.

"That's good and what about this one?" I asked, peering at the image on the screen.

"This is Tanya," Philip answered. "She looks like she has a single lamb; is that right, Sally?" Sally nodded, pointing out the little form displayed on the screen, which I decided needed the expert eye to distinguish.

"Very nice," I said indulgently. "So, why do we need to scan the sheep?"

"If they are carrying twins, we know we need to feed them better so that they don't get 'twin lamb disease'," Philip was keen to explain.

"Hmmm...and how can you tell if any have 'twin lamb disease'?" I asked.

"Well, the mother would get very skinny and start to waste away," Philip related what he had learned from his studies on sheep rearing as he passed the next sheep into the cradle. "You need to feel the ribs if you suspect a problem; like this….." he explained as he demonstrated on the ewe. "In the later stages, ketones could build up in her body, and there would be the smell of 'pear drops' on her breath, indicating that she urgently needs high-quality feed." Sally sat back on her low stool and smiled at me over her mug of tea; she did not seem to mind Philip practising his 'veterinary skills'.

"Now this one is empty," Sally announced, reading the screen as she scanned the next sheep.

"That's OK; she is only a two-year-old, and she can go to the butcher's as 'hogget'," Philip replied nonchalantly. I looked pityingly at the poor barren ewe, pleased for her that she did not understand English. I decided it was time to go back into the house to hug my baby and to check her breath for the smell of pear drops.

It was 2 am on a clear, frosty night as Philip walked towards the footpath in the top fields, heading for *Tŷ'n Gorse*. Molly had sounded urgent on the telephone:

"We're 'aving a raight difficult lambing, Philip; David says he needs your 'elp!"

"I will be right there, Molly!" Philip had replied, hastily dressing and donning his wax jacket, tweed hat and rubber boots. Seizing a torch from the cupboard, he left the warmth of the home, where the kitchen light glowed enticingly behind him. Although it was bitterly cold, he decided it would be quicker and cause less of a disturbance to the neighbourhood if he walked the half-mile to Dave and Molly's farm across the fields rather than drive the three miles around the country lanes.

Gazing in wonderment at the night sky, he marched on swiftly, clambered over the five-bar gate leading to the top fields and cut a dark trail through the sparkling, frosty whiteness of the rough pasture. There was no need to use the torch for, although it was a moonless night, the stars and the Milky Way shone so brightly that it was easy to follow the beaten path, which glittered in the stellar light. Suddenly, he saw a bright light coming straight towards him. It started as a speck, became the size of a pea, then the size of a football, then exploded as a massive, brilliant burst of white light in front of him! His eyes were dazzled for a few seconds, and then there was darkness again; there had been no sound, just total silence! Still reeling from the experience, Philip tried to make sense of what he had seen. He had often watched shooting stars crossing the skies on clear nights, but to have one burst before him like that was a memory he would treasure forever!

When Philip arrived at *Tŷ'n Gorse*, he was pleased to see that Dave had already brought the labouring ewe into one of the well-lit stables. She now lay exhausted on the clean, fresh straw with her lamb's swollen black head protruding from her rear end. Dave had found her two hours earlier in that predicament, but despite his best efforts, he could not budge the poor, stuck creature. In some cases, the head could be pushed back inside the ewe to pull out the forelegs at the same time as the head, but there was no hope of that being possible at this late stage.

"Even I can't get my hand inside her," Molly said despondently, holding up her petite hands to demonstrate.

"Aye, we've lost this lamb, Molly," Dave said, shaking his head sadly. "And 'ee were a raight bonny lamb!" It was indeed a sad situation. "What is to be done, Philip?" Dave's face looked drawn and tired as he raised his bushy eyebrows, hopefully in Philip's direction. Philip knew what had to be done, and turned to wash his hands in the bucket of warm water and carbolic soap Molly had placed by the door. Molly decided to leave him with the grisly task of cutting off the head of the dead lamb in the hope of saving the ewe.

"Not a nice job for you tonight, Philip," Molly apologized as she poured the two men a welcome cup of tea in the soothing warmth of her cosy kitchen.

"No, but we saved the ewe, and she is a good sheep," Philip replied, trying to be positive. "We gave her a shot of antibiotics in case of infection, and she has water there to drink for when she feels a bit stronger, so she should be fine now."

"We put that bobby lamb that you have been bottle feeding to her straight away, and she is letting him suckle," Dave was pleased to give Molly at least some good news.

"Well, that's raight good that she 'as accepted 'im," Molly replied, "I felt raight sorry for 'im when 'is mother died, poor little mite. But didn't the vet say she was 'aving twins David?" Molly asked.

"There was no other lamb inside her, Molly; I made sure of that," Philip responded.

"But when Sally scanned this ewe, she said she could see twins, David, so that was why we were feeding 'er oop," Molly persisted.

"Seems to me the scanning is helpful but not 100 per cent accurate," Philip interjected.

"Yes, Sally said that when we did the scanning, didn't she, Philip?" Dave replied. "She was spot on with all the others, but this one was a surprise."

"That is the risk of running the Suffolk ram with the Llyn breed of ewes, I believe," Philip stated. "Twin births are not a problem, but these single lambs are just too big."

"I think you are right, Philip; these Suffolks with their big black heads don't make for easy lambing," Dave concurred.

"My Welsh ewes are even smaller than your Llyn Peninsulas, so Mr Davies recommended that I run the Beulah ram with them. He produces good-sized lambs with small heads, so I will be keeping all his ewe lambs for breeding." Dave nodded thoughtfully at Philip's comments while Molly poured them another cup of tea.

"Hey, I must tell you what happened on my way to you tonight!" Philip brightened as he took another biscuit and began to relate his incredible experience with the shooting star.

23 Piggies

"Let's not tell them," I suggested as Philip and I watched Daniel, Amelia and Joshua vying with each other to feed carrots through the gate to the three little piglets. "I don't want them to be upset."

John Owen had told us about the piglets produced by the Large White sow belonging to a couple for whom he had been doing some fencing work. Roy was a deep-sea diver by trade, while Millicent ran a thriving enterprise as a talented seamstress from their cottage, *Hafod Las,* on the Mountain road between Llanfechell and the top of Mynydd Mechell.

"You could fatten a few up for the freezer or even sell them," John had suggested, discretely out of earshot of the children.

The young weaners had bounced excitedly from the back of Roy's pick-up truck when released into one of our fields for their first open-air experience. After tracing out their boundaries and snuffling about amongst the undergrowth lining the walls of their new surroundings, they soon discovered their corrugated iron house tucked into one of the corners of the paddock, filled with fresh straw. Their squeals of delight were a pleasure to hear, and Philip was so pleased to witness their appreciation for all his preparations. He was familiar with raising pigs, as his father had kept pigs on their Hampshire smallholding, and when he was a teenager, he had worked in intensive pig farming. Philip mulled over that latter experience with distaste. He decided to include me in his musings as we watched our children becoming acquainted with their new 'pets'.

"Did I tell you the story about the sow that broke free? She was taken to meet the boar, but she decided against his proposition," he began relating the story with a chuckle. "Jumped right over the pen wall and charged off she did, leaving the poor boar bewildered and insulted! Unfortunately, I met her halfway along a narrow alleyway; she was coming at me full pelt, and absolutely nothing was going to stop her!" He started laughing at the memory, and the children turned around to hear the story.

"So, what did you do?" I asked, alarmed at the thought for I knew just how powerful a full-grown pig could be.

"Well, I tried to stop her, but she was so huge and determined that she ran straight between my legs, carrying me off backwards, riding on her back!" A small gasp rippled through Philip's audience.

"How did you get off, Dad?" Daniel asked with rapt interest.

"It was a pretty scary experience, I must say, but I just held on to the hair of her back for all I was worth, with the knees on my  overalls being almost shredded to bits as they scuffed along the concrete walls of the alleyway. It was getting a bit painful, I can tell you!" Philip's animated account had a rewarding effect as the children listened raptly.

"Then what happened, Daddy?" Amelia chipped in.

"When we got to the end of the alleyway, she threw me off, and I landed in a big pile of straw and pig muck!" Everyone laughed at that account as we walked back to the house to check on our sleeping Saffron and to prepare for the evening meal.

"Tell us some more piggy stories please, Daddy," the children begged as we sat around the table.

"OK," Philip answered when he finished a mouthful of sausage plait, "but I think you had better finish your dinner first; this story may put you off eating." Everyone rapidly complied.

"Well, my good friend, Roger Drury, got me a job at an intensive pig farm, rather like a factory, and I worked there for just a few months," Philip began his story with a wrinkling of his nose at the unpleasant memory of the experience. "Pigs are far too intelligent to be raised that way. They were grouped six to a pen at about three months old, but of course, they quickly grew bigger and bigger. They would do their toilet in an adjoining sector, with steel grating for a floor, as they liked to keep their concreted sleeping area clean and dry. Drinking water was always available for them, and they quickly learned how to bite a lever on the tap to release the water straight into their mouths. Four times a day, their meals of powdered mixed grains with dried fishmeal would automatically be dropped down through a chute onto the concrete floor for them to eat; it was a never-changing diet, always dull and uninteresting. Sadly, they had almost no human contact; there was nothing to do or to play with, day after day, and they looked seriously bored."

"Aaw," the children chorused; "that is so sad, poor piggies!" Philip nodded in agreement and continued his tale.

"As a consequence, they would often turn to bullying and fighting amongst themselves, causing a lot of pain, misery and injury to each other. I suggested to Mike, the farm manager, that we throw a rubber tyre or something into each pen, so they could play games with it between themselves to occupy their intelligent brains, like the piggy version of rugby. But he said they were only animals and did not need entertaining." Amelia's sense of justice got the better of her at this point; she jumped off her chair, frowned hard and, with her arms akimbo, she stamped her foot on the kitchen floor.

"The mean man!" she stated with feeling.

"Anyway, one day, the pigs in one of the pens decided to stage a Great Escape," Philip continued. "They managed to dislodge the

179

iron floor grating, and all six pigs dropped down into the filthy mire below! Thankfully, it had been mostly pumped out on the previous day, so it was not as bad as it could have been. Still, by the time someone had noticed what had happened, the pigs were so covered in black gunge that we could only see six pairs of blinking, white-rimmed, brown eyes peering up at us." The children thought that was hilarious. "Understandably, no one wanted the job of retrieving those large, slippery beasts, but we agreed that, Mike, the farm manager, should be the one sent down into that murky cavern. I wondered if, as he climbed down the ladder, he wished he had given the pigs a tyre to play with."

"So, what happened next, Dad?" Daniel asked, and everyone listened with rapt attention to the answer.

"There was a lot of squishing, squelching and squealing as Mike waded through the sewerage and tried to grab the slippery pigs. All we could see from the top were six sets of brown eyes and one set of blue eyes looking up at us from amongst that horrible, smelly filth!"

"Euw! Yuk! Disgusting!" was the reaction from Philip's audience, and I was duly pleased that we had finished our meal before hearing the recounting of that revolting event.

"So, how did the man get them out?" I had to know.

"Mike managed to get a rope around them one at a time, then Roger and I were able to haul them up, hose them off and repair the pen for them," Philip answered with a mixture of triumph and disgust.

"And did they give the pigs a tyre to play with after that, Daddy?" Amelia asked, leaning her little blond head adoringly against her Daddy's arm.

"I would like to think so, Amelia, but I don't know" he replied, stroking her hair gently. "I hated that factory farming so much that I quit working there very soon after that happened."

"But our piggies will not be raised that way, will they?" I reassured the children. "You will be able to give them treats every day, and we will make sure to change the straw in their shed regularly, won't we?" Daniel, Amelia and Joshua nodded in agreement.

Feeding pigs can be prohibitively expensive; thankfully, however, through a friendly contact, we arranged to have all the leftovers from an Italian restaurant in Bangor, so pizza crusts and spaghetti were a big part of their diet. In addition, we turned out the vegetable peelings into their field, which they rapidly devoured, except for parsnips, which, for some reason, they would never touch.

"So, what have you decided to call your piggies?" I asked the children at dinner time one evening. They had evidently been considering names for the young pigs as the two boys turned to Amelia, who appeared to be the delegated spokesperson, and they gave her a nod.

"Pork, Ham and Bacon!" she replied decisively, and both boys nodded in confirmation of the decision.

"Oh, I see." Philip and I looked at each other in surprise.

"No delusions there then!"

24 Cheating Death

"Sorry, Love, but I have to leave you to keep an eye on the sheep today, and one of them is in labour." Philip had been up early and done the rounds of the top fields before going to work on the Wind Farm tree-planting contract for Anglesey Mowers. Thankfully, he had the use of the company pick-up truck, leaving me the car available so I could take the children to school. "We managed to bring her down, and she is just over the wall here." He took off his hat, hung his wax jacket on the back of the door and stood at the kitchen window, looking out towards the paddock between our house and *Bryn Llyn*.

"We did a good job, didn't we, Jill?" Philip said over his shoulder as he washed his hands at the sink. Jill, who had been panting heavily in her bed by the Rayburn, turned blissful eyes towards her master and managed the nearest thing to a broad, ingratiating smile while her long, bushy tail beat a happy rhythm on the kitchen floor. "The ewe should be fine, but just keep an eye on her, please," Philip added as he joined the children at the breakfast table.

I had watched him delivering lambs and had taken the lambing course earlier in the year, so I knew all the theories should there be a need for my intervention. I hoped there would not be however, as I was still quite nervous about managing my first lambing on my own. Apart from that, I had arranged to meet Candy in Cemaes after dropping our children to school, as I had agreed to look after her two young visitors from Hampshire while she went to work. Julie and Dawn had another week of the spring school holiday left, and they were so excited to have the opportunity to come up to the farm before returning home.

With baby Saffron installed in the car and the last of the children chivvied to join her, I peered over the concrete wall to check on the labouring ewe. She was grazing contentedly in the paddock, seemingly unaware of the little dark head poking out from her rear end. Just then, she lay down on her side and started to heave, and it looked as though she could do with some help. Mustering courage and with a few minutes to spare before leaving to take the children to school, I clambered over the stile leading to the paddock and started walking towards her.

However, I was dealing with one of the wilder Welsh Mountain sheep here, so as soon as she saw me, she was up and running madly around the perimeter of the temporary fencing that Philip had erected. There was nothing I could do other than stand and watch her crazed cavorting as she took a running leap and hurled herself against the fence. Jill, who was watching from the top of the wall, suddenly jumped into the paddock, attempting to bring the ewe back under control. She and her Master had worked hard to round her up that morning, so she would not allow her to escape now.

Unfortunately, Poppy wanted to join in the fun too. Before I could stop her, she also hopped down from her position on the wall where she had been spectating beside Jill and started barking and scampering around haphazardly in the paddock, causing total, unhelpful chaos!

The ewe became even more frenzied, and after doing two more circuits of her pen, she took another dive at the fence, breaking it down, and then she charged off back to the top fields. Jill was intent on following her, but I called her back, and we stood together watching as the frightened animal galloped across the horizon like a two-headed apparition, with her lamb's head bobbing up and down and with a disobedient little Poppy, running and yapping behind her. I was not relishing coming home from school to deal with either of those uncooperative characters.

Work on renovating the cottages in the village of Llanfechell was already well underway, causing considerable disruption to traffic at the crossroads by the Post Office as I returned from Cemaes with my young wards. I knew it was all for a good cause, but I was getting rather impatient and anxious about the task awaiting me at home as we sat waiting for the man with the Stop/Go sign to give us the green Go ahead.

Being town-born and bred, Julie and Dawn were in awe and wonder at country customs and antics. It was perhaps just as well that they were there that day to look after little Saffron and to keep Poppy under control while Jill and I ran around the nine acres of top fields in pursuit of our runaway ewe. The memories of my recent lambing course flooded through my mind as I ran to the far reaches of our land...

The windowless outhouse of the old stone farmhouse had been cold, damp and oozing morbidity as we small group of would-be shepherds entered. The officiating vet in his white coat stood beside some large, oblong wooden boxes perched on the trestle tables, which we learned represented the hindquarters of a birthing ewe. He was a man possibly in his mid-forties, with a smooth complexion and streaks of grey in his receding blond, curly hair. His assistant immediately distributed some rubber gloves and polythene aprons while the vet prepared to explain the various techniques of dealing with difficult births. With a broad smile on his handsome face, the vet whipped out from one of the boxes the tiny limp carcass of a dead lamb and held it aloft, like a magician producing a rabbit from a top hat. Everyone in the room winced but tried not to appear shocked, which I thought disappointed him.

'Well, this means business!' I said to myself, and turning on my heel, I marched objectively to the far corner of the room to take off my coat and deposit my handbag on a small stone shelf that jutted out from the wall. Walking back towards the group by the tables, I stopped in my tracks as I was greeted by an array of male faces, all staring expectantly at me.

'No, I was not planning on fainting!' My expression reassured them as I rolled up my sleeves, and they all hastily returned their attention to the gruesome task at hand.

"Away! Come by!" I knew the commands Philip had taught Jill, but as we chased after the escaped ewe that morning, only Jill seemed to know which meant go to the left and which meant go to the right. After a while, I had confused her so much that she disappeared, leaving me running around the acreage on my own, with 'Away!' and 'Come by!' commands wafting across the rocky outcrops, and with no one but me to obey them. I later found her skulking behind a low stone wall, hoping I would not notice that she had given up on me. It was at that point that I decided I was going to need some extra help.

There was no sound coming from the old caravan at the back of *Bryn Llyn*, where our neighbours, Leslie and Heulwen, lived, and I feared I was calling too early. However, I was in dire need of support for my dilemma, so I knocked gently on the side of the caravan. There was no answer, so I rapped hard on the caravan door. The silence inside was suddenly shattered by my intrusion and was followed by a loud grunt; the caravan then rocked markedly as someone stumbled about noisily and crashed against the inside wall. I wondered if I should beat a hasty retreat at the sound of the commotion that ensued.

"It's me, Lynnette, Leslie!" I called out, trying to ease his confusion. "Sorry to bother you."

"Doo! Doo!" and other incomprehensible mutterings came from inside, then silence. After several moments, I considered giving up on this option and started heading back towards the garden gate when suddenly the caravan door swung open. Leslie had probably needed a little time to compose himself, and there he stood in the caravan doorway in his blue and white stripy pyjamas, with his flat cloth cap pulled firmly down on his head.

By the time Leslie and Heulwen arrived on the scene, Jill had managed to bring the errant sheep back down to the lower fields around the house without my assistance. She crouched menacingly on the ground, locking the ewe into submission with piercing, intense amber eyes. That sheep knew who was now in control, and she was going nowhere. Meanwhile, Julie and Dawn were enjoying playing little nursemaids to Saffron and had her all wrapped up in her pushchair while they watched the performance with fascination.

I was very grateful for my neighbours' help; between us, we managed to drive the sheep, with her limp, protruding lamb's head, into the pen by the old barn. With one deft and masterful sweep, Leslie laid her down on the ground and held her in place. Heulwen, standing with the rest of our supporters and watching expectantly from behind the farm gate, quivered noticeably with pride and admiration at her husband's display of manly capability. I washed my hands carefully in the bucket of warm, soapy water that Julie had brought for me and bent down to give a gentle word of encouragement to my labouring lady. Having given birth to four children, I knew how much I had appreciated such soothing and reassuring words from my precious midwives. Now, successfully delivering a dead lamb from the plasticised depths of a wooden box was one thing, but here was the real thing; a lamb with a swollen head, a lolling blue tongue and a mother who was still pushing hard with each contraction.

"Slide the fingers under the lamb's chin and insert the hand gently into the uterus," the vet's words were ringing in my ears as I recalled his instructions. Perhaps that would work if the lamb's head had not had several hours of swelling time; however, there was very little 'inserting' space even for my hand. No wonder the shepherds we had spoken to had cringed at the size of Philip's hands!

"Don't worry, lady," I crooned, hoping to sound reassuring as the distressed ewe attempted to look beyond Leslie's knees at what I was doing. A light rain began to set in, but our audience stayed captivated by their posts.

"Ah, I can feel a front knee!" I announced, continuing my running commentary, more for myself than anyone else. 'Cup the little hoofs to prevent them from tearing at the mother's vagina', the vet had said. "Yes; one leg out!" Thankfully, it was easy to find the other front knee, which was also jammed against the pelvic wall. "Two legs out!" That was easier than I had expected. "Now pull on both legs,"....and out slid a large, part-Beulah lamb. Laying the limp figure with its swollen head on the grass, I gave its mother a pat on her head, and she started to 'whicker' lovingly to her new-born. 'Clear the nose and mouth and massage the chest area if there appears to be no life,' I recalled the next stage of instructions. Nothing! No response at all! 'Tickle the nostrils with a piece of straw to make it sneeze.' Oh, how I wished! Still no response.

The rain was getting heavier as our audience pulled up the hoods on their coats and on Saffron's pushchair. Poppy, attached by her lead to the pushchair, managed to shelter under a bush that hung over the garden wall, but Jill's attention was riveted conscientiously on the current task. I really wanted this event to have a happy outcome for the watching girls, so in desperation, I gathered up the lifeless little form by its back legs, swung it three times around my head, and then resumed pumping its chest as it lay on the grass beside its mother. Leslie looked sympathetically at me and released the ewe to see if she could do anything to help.

She seemed understandably exhausted and disappointed, so she laid her head back on the ground dejectedly.

"Julie," I said, suddenly remembering something else from my course. "Would you mind fetching me a glass of cold water, please?" Julie returned speedily with the cold water, pleased to be doing something to help. Raising one of the lamb's soft and furry black ears, I trickled in a little of the liquid. Miraculously, the ear twitched, the head shook violently, the 'dead' lamb sneezed, took a deep breath and started calling to its mother.

"It's alive!" I said with sheer delight and exuberance. A cheer went up, Leslie and Heulwen beamed broad smiles, and the girls jumped up and down with joy. The rain was pouring down by then, and according to the girls, my makeup was streaming down my face. I did not care; my mission was a success, for that little lamb had cheated death and was very much alive!

The ewe raised her head and began to lick her offspring clean as it nursed at her bulging teats. I bent over to rub her head gently and covered her with my anorak; our eyes met, and I knew she was saying, 'Thank you!'

25 Fair Exchange

They were stately animals, half Suffolk, half Welsh, and they belonged to our friends, Geoff and Yvonne, a couple originally from our home area in the south of England. They now lived in a cosy, well-presented whitewashed cottage in the hamlet of Cerrig Mân, at the foot of Parys Mountain. It was a mutually advantageous arrangement; Philip could graze our sheep on their small acreage in exchange for caring for Tag and her mother, Mutton, on the condition that neither sheep should ever go to the butchers. Philip was fascinated with the history of Parys Mountain, so as we were visiting nearby that day, we managed to persuade Geoff and Yvonne to join us for a walk up the mountain.

It was like a moonscape on the mountain, unearthly, with the only plant life seen growing amongst the shallow gravel being the muted greens and vibrant purples of the wind-buffeted heather. Bright red and ochre-tinted rocks flanked the disused tramway along which we walked, where lumps of 'fool's gold' and Chalcopyrite glinted colourfully in the afternoon sunshine. Some recent work on the mine was in evidence, with brand new pit-head winding gear set up to sink a new shaft, and a stream of acidic water drained the mountain's maze of ancient mines, flowing rusty-red and lifeless into man-made ponds. From there the stream continued to flow down, through Amlwch as the *Afon Goch* (or Red River), then out into the sea via Amlwch Port. Geoff, who had done a lot of research on the history of Parys Mountain, was keen to relate some interesting information.

"Did you know mining on this mountain goes back as far as the early Bronze Age? In Roman times it was the world leader in copper production, and a couple of hundred years ago, this was a thriving industry; the mine owners even minted their own copper money to pay the workers. During the last century, thousands of tons of scrap iron were brought in each year by ship and train, and thrown into those ponds down there," Geoff informed us, pointing towards the rectangular pools alongside the path.

"What was the purpose of the scrap iron?" I asked.

"It is simple chemistry," Geoff was happy to explain. "The acid water from the mines is saturated with dissolved copper, and when it encounters the scrap iron, the acid greedily dissolves it. But it must first put down the copper in exchange, which can be harvested later from the pond bed as copper cake. So, if there were no scrap iron, the copper would go down the stream and out to sea."

Yvonne and I did the typical paranoid mother thing, gathering the children close just in case they may have considered leaping into those hazardous pools. The wind was strengthening and becoming more hostile, echoing menacingly, as it whirled around and collided with the sculptured walls of that 'lunar' terrain. Yvonne suggested we all return to their house for a cup of tea.

Photo Credit Copper Kingdom https://copperkingdom.co.u

News of the arrangement Philip had come to with Geoff and Yvonne quickly spread amongst their retired English acquaintances. We soon found ourselves adopting a growing flock, along with several small parcels of pasture and an increasing number of good friends. It was by this means that we came to know the unforgettable Glen Howard.

Bill and Brenda Carter came from Oxfordshire and now lived in a whitewashed, stone-built cottage on the main road to Bangor. Bill had been a professional Big Band singer in his younger years. He was a cheerful man in his late sixties, with a constant twinkle of merriment and good intent in his eyes, and both he and Brenda loved our children from our first meeting.

Now the French Charolais sheep has no hope of being highest on my list of attractive sheep, and the Carter's Becky did nothing to improve my opinion. She had a short, thick fleece, almost hairless face and legs, with buttocks enormous enough to turn the head of a lusty hippopotamus! For some reason, Becky had a crippled neck in a permanently lowered and twisted position. However, she was their adored pet and made Philip promise that in return for grazing our sheep on their pasture, he would care for poor Becky for the rest of her life.

With the business matters agreed upon, we were all sitting at the picnic table in Bill and Brenda's back garden enjoying their hospitality when suddenly a large Alsatian cross-bred dog bounded around the corner of the house. Upon seeing us, it stopped in its tracks, stood stock-still and set steely eyes on we strangers, then it started barking loudly, causing us considerable alarm.

"Heinz! Get behind!" The man who next appeared from around the corner was clearly in control of this fear-provoking animal, for the dog instantly obeyed, dropping onto the ground behind him. "Sorry about that," the man said as he eyed the array of shocked faces turned in his direction. "He would not hurt you...... unless I gave him.... the Word!" A conspiratorial look crossed his face as though daring us to ask what that 'Word' might happen to be. We decided against it, just in case. The man, who appeared to be in his mid-to-late thirties, was tall and well-built with an almost black military haircut, close-cropped beard and moustache, and alert, brown eyes behind his dark-rimmed sunglasses.

"Ah, Glen," Brenda exclaimed. "This is the Barlow family, Philip, Lynnette and their children. Come and have a cup of tea with us." Glen reached over the table, shook Philip's hand confidently, gave me a respectful nod of acknowledgement and swept our children's awed faces with an unexpectedly warm smile.

"Glen Howard," he introduced himself, with a pleasant trace of Welsh in his voice. "I am staying in the caravan at the back until I find a house," he explained, removing a brick-sized portable telephone from his pocket and placing it on the table beside his car keys. He sat down on the bench next to Brenda, who handed him his cup of tea and offered him a biscuit. Heinz crept closer to the table, hoping for the same treatment. "Heinz! Get down!" Glen commanded, and the dog instantly dropped to the ground beside him.

"Will he have a biscuit?" Brenda asked, and Heinz's eyes began to melt with appealing anticipation. Glen took the biscuit from Betty and balanced it on Heinz's outstretched forelegs. The dog looked down at it and then at Glen, awaiting his command.

"Wait, wait," Glen warned, and the dog dutifully obeyed, his eyes switching between the biscuit and his master's face. "Have it!" said Glen, and the biscuit disappeared with one gulp.

"Wow! Do you think we could try that with Jill?" I asked with admiration.

"Would he have let you take it off him?" Philip asked.

"Try it," Glen challenged, repeating the exercise with another biscuit. Philip moved closer and gingerly reached his hand toward the dog's forelegs. Heinz locked eyes with Philip, bared his teeth and snarled threateningly. Philip wisely backed off!

"He is a trained security dog," Glen explained. "So, he will not eat anything unless I tell him to, but he knows his rights."

During the next while, we learned a bit about Glen's history; he was originally from Conwy and had pursued a career in the RAF as an avionics specialist until he retired due to a back injury. After that, he worked in the Middle East, teaching the utilisation of high-tech security systems. Perhaps that would account for his acute sense of vigilance, for his eyes would frequently scan his surroundings as though he were always on alert and prepared for the unexpected.

Eventually, Glen bought a house in Amlwch Port, although his work in electronic security surveillance took him across most of North Wales and always in the company of Heinz, his constant friend and protector. Our paths were to cross frequently after that first meeting. Although we perceived him as primarily a military-minded man, we found Glen to have a keen sense of humour and loved to laugh and play tricks on people in a good-hearted way. With his dark glasses, loose-fitting black leather jacket and black Mazda sports car, Daniel, Amelia and Joshua were in constant awe of him as though he had just stepped out of Hollywood.

26 Movie in the Making

"Well, you would have thought they would have been satisfied, but no, they want it back just as it was!" Mrs Jones was holding court in a crowded Post Office one morning in late May. Many villagers were there, either in the hope of learning the contents of the parish council meeting held the evening before if they had not been in attendance, or they were keen to contribute to the discussion if they had been. The village-proud local councillors, who had eagerly anticipated the return of the film company, had been severely crestfallen at the shocked and disappointed reaction they had received on the presentation of their gloriously renovated village!

Old Mr Selwyn Parry was clutching a small paper bag of his favourite cough candy sweets and trying to make out what was being said.

"Would you believe it? The film company are not at all pleased with all the improvements made to the village, Mr Parry; they want it to look just the same as it did when they came here last year!" Mrs Owen, whose husband ran the local garage, was repeating the news very loudly into Mr Parry's ear. Mr Parry was looking quite bewildered.

"Don't like it?" he retorted; "well, what's wrong with it?"

"There's nothing wrong with it, Mr Parry," Mrs Jones assured him, attempting to regain command of her audience. "Your cottage looks lovely with its new windows and roof."

"The best Welsh slate tiles we have too," Mrs Pritchard, his neighbour, contributed. "Came special from Penrhyn they did!"

A jumble of protesting comments erupted, along with much pointing out through the Post Office window.

"And just look at the War Memorial," said Mrs Williams from *Y Cefn Glas* pub. "I don't remember seeing it look that clean for years!" The War Memorial did indeed look clean and splendid; in fact, it was now possible to make out the features on the face of the soldier atop it, and it was much easier to see the time through the brightly polished glass on the clock.

A lot of noise and disruption had caused difficulties for the village and for the traffic needing to pass through it over the previous months. Much hard work had gone into hacking off the plaster from the walls of the cottages opposite the post office, although some of it had just crumbled off as it was so old. Now, with the solid stonework revealed and repointed, the cottages looked quite charming. Unfortunately, all the changes meant the village did not present the drab and dismal setting the film company needed to tell its sad story convincingly. Therefore, as it was already committed to using the village square for some of its movie scenes, the company was permitted to use whatever reasonable means possible to reinstate the village to its previous dowdy appearance.

It took the movie company almost the whole month of June to restore the village to the way it had caught the eye of the movie scouts the previous year. The villagers watched in dismay as the walls of the row of cottages were wallpapered on the *outside* and then painted a dull grey. A hefty dose of sooty sludge was carefully spread over the roofs and the new double-glazed windows so that they lost all their recent lustre and the old cottages began to take on that familiar gloominess again. The re-blackened clock on the War Memorial was hard to read, and according to our postman, the church minister was none too pleased about the coating of grime that now covered the recently whitewashed walls of the churchyard.

Much to the delight of everyone, however, July began to get very warm, everyone that is, except the director and film crew that had come to Llanfechell to make the long-awaited 'Russian movie'.

When the movie scouts chose the village as the perfect setting the previous autumn, the weather had been anything but warm and sunny. Therefore, they did not expect that the summer weather would bring out swarms of visitors to the Island, nearly all of whom wanted to pass through the little village of Llanfechell. It was particularly busy at those times of day when frantic parents needed to get children to and from school, but impossible when it was School Sports Day!

Mr Jones, the headmaster of the English-speaking school in Cemaes Bay, was very well-meaning and likeable, although inclined to be easily distracted. His school was a healthy blend of various cultures, based on the principle of zero tolerance of racial prejudice. Our children enjoyed the relaxed atmosphere there, and they all seemed tranquil and happy as they mingled amongst the periphery of spectators on the school sports field. All in attendance chattered excitedly in either Welsh or with a medley of various English accents as they awaited the start of the day's events. We knew many of the competing schoolchildren and their families well, so there would be a lot of cheering and encouragement to be done.

A hand-held megaphone called everyone to attention as Mr Jones, after a short welcome and a word of encouragement for the children to do their best, announced that the Cemaes Bay School Sports Day had officially begun.

"May we have the first competitors please?" Mr Jones' megaphone blasted out. Daniel, who had always disliked any competitive sports, was clawing at the newly cut grass as he lay on his back amongst his classmates on the sports field, just a few yards from where my parents and I sat on our low wooden school chairs. I hated to see him so nervous.

"*Un... dau...tri...*" Mr Jones counted slowly and deliberately through his megaphone. The children were beginning to perspire with increasing nervousness under the hot sun. Mr Jones had just raised the starting gun, ready to fire into the air when one of the teachers tapped him on the shoulder and handed him an 'urgent' note.

"Oh, just one moment," he mumbled into the megaphone before reading the note aloud. "Would the owner of the brown Ford Cortina with the number plate.............please return to your vehicle? You have left your lights on." There was a groan of complaint and a rustling of handbags as parents searched for their car keys, and those who owned Ford Cortinas went to check on their cars.

"Now, where were we?" Mr Jones muttered to himself as he lifted the megaphone again. "Oh, yes; are you ready?" Were they ever ready? The poor little mites still lying on the ground were about fainting from the heat and anxiety!

"Un... dau...tri..." Bang! The starter gun burst a sonic boom through the megaphone beside it; the children scrambled to their feet and raced towards the pile of shoes they had discarded in disorderly fashion at the far end of the sports field. The winners were the first to find their shoes, put them on and arrive back at the starting point.

"Mum, Mum!" Amelia was twitching at my elbow as the beanbag throwing got into full swing. "The elastic in my shorts has broken!"

'Oh, no! I meant to mend those shorts before Sports Day,' I berated myself. Her Nanny, with her 'multipurpose' handbag, started rummaging in its depths for a safety pin but could only come up with a sturdy hairgrip. Nine-month-old Saffron was in no position to relinquish the safety pin she was wearing on her terry nappy, and I had no spare ones in her nappy bag that day.

Amelia's shorts seemed to be holding up well with her hairgrip remedy, we noted, as we anxiously watched her race past us on the sports field with her blond ponytail swinging from side to side. She was considerably taller than many of her competitors, so she quickly reached third place as her long slim legs pounded the ground.

"Come on, Amelia! Come on, Amelia!" we shouted. "She is going to win! She is! She is going to win!" Yes, she was in the lead, heading for the finishing line, when suddenly, the hairgrip on her shorts must have fallen off, for they started to slide down her thighs. We watched open-mouthed as she grabbed at them and took a leap across the finishing line. A burst of laughter and applause ensued, but she did not care; she had achieved first place, despite the sagging shorts!

Daniel excelled at the long jump, while Joshua would have achieved first or second place in his race had he not stopped just before the finishing line when he noticed his best friend was lagging way behind.

"Come on, Ryan!" he shouted, and five little racers shot past him to the winning post. I was rather proud of him for his thoughtfulness. Ice creams were bought from a busy vendor parked in the small lane beside the school and distributed by indulgent parents or grandparents to the thirsty participants. My father had spent the afternoon pushing Saffron up and down in her pushchair on the grass behind the rows of spectators and feeding her ice lollies until she was a sticky but happy mess.

The Mothers' race was announced as the concluding event of the day; however, Daniel shook his head at me with a pleading expression.

"You don't need to run in the Mothers' race, Mum," he assured me tactfully. He was still embarrassed by the memory of my unsuccessful efforts at his first School Sports Day in Hampshire. I got his point, so I stayed in my chair, choosing to cheer on those brave ladies who did contend. Mrs Owen, the deputy headmistress, used the megaphone to give the children instructions for the wooden chairs to be collected, while Mr Jones handed out some medals to the winners. Mr Jones gave Mrs Owen a look of reproach as he retrieved his megaphone and attempted to regain control of the thinning, disorderly crowd and call a congratulatory conclusion to the happy day. Yes, it had been a happy day, we all thought, as we said goodbye to my parents and our friends, before driving homeward through the country lanes in the sweltering heat.

We were not the only ones suffering from the heat, however. Back in the village square of Llanfechell, the patience of the film director was being stretched to the limit. Parked cars lined the approach to the village, while some members of the film company stood with 'Stop' signs to control the traffic. The car park behind *Y Cefn Glas* was full of abandoned vehicles, as their occupants flocked to the cordoned-off perimeters of the village square to watch the actors being filmed in front of the War Memorial.

Considering that the setting on this abnormally hot and windless day was supposed to represent a cold, grey experience in Russia, the poor actors were sweltering in their thick sheepskin coats, hats, gloves and high leather boots. The scenes should only have taken a short while to film, but the unfortunate timing meant it was taking far longer than expected. The traffic was increasing, and the crowd began to swell as more children were collected from school, while one or two of them managed to escape from their mothers to try to be part of the show.

"Cut!" The director shouted as their mothers attempted to retrieve the little rascals. The school buses began to arrive with the older children from the senior school in Amlwch, which caused even more congestion. The bus drivers tried to swing their long vehicles as unobtrusively as possible through the junction, unloading more swarms of youthful spectators. I had no idea that so many people claimed to live in the local villages. Amelia was craning her neck to look over the dashboard at the fascinating spectacle, while Joshua and Saffron were already fast asleep in the back seats beside Daniel.

"Mum! That lady is waving at you," Daniel suddenly alerted, tapping me urgently on the shoulder.

"Which lady?" I asked.

"That lady over there," he replied, pointing at the film director who was gesticulating wildly on the far side of the square. Unfortunately, mesmerized by all the distractions, I had driven into the middle of the junction on a 'Stop' sign, managing to cause a total traffic jam! I felt a flush of embarrassment colour my already sun-bronzed face when I became aware of my predicament. I slowly wound down the car window as the director lady marched purposely towards me, her white cotton blouse carefully tucked into her tight beige trousers and attempting to cling to her perspiring body. She swept back her thick, shoulder-length, sandy-blond hair from her forehead, and as she leaned on the ledge of my opened window, the car was infused with the heady aroma of her steaming perfume. All eyes were suddenly on me, instead of the hot and uncomfortable actors, as though I were privileged to be in the presence of a Celebrity!

"Would you mind driving back, please, Madam?" the director asked with the sweetest synthetic smile. It was evident that the long-suffering lady director was finding it necessary to call upon every scrap of 'idiot-relations' training she had received to be able to deal with me. Amelia, who was all smiles and curiosity, watched the lady with interest, but Daniel was mortified and slid down as low as possible in the back seat.

"Oh, of course," I replied, somewhat self-consciously but relieved to be let off so lightly. I noticed the cluster of people gathered in front of the Post Office was watching the situation with ill-disguised amusement. Between the crowd and the director, however, I suddenly spotted THE CAMERA, and I was instantly Star struck!

"Yes, certainly," I replied with exaggerated enthusiasm and with what I imagined to be a gleaming and captivating smile. "Would you like me to be reversing like this or like this?" I asked, tossing back my head and running my fingers through my hair as though auditioning for the part. The director gripped the ledge of the open car window, fixing me with a threatening stare as her lips tightened and her eyes narrowed menacingly in her seriously reddening face!

"Just reverse?" I offered weakly. The steady, steely look on her face said it all. "Just reverse," I answered my own question. And I did.

Despite everything, the movie was eventually produced and could be seen on the television screen in the hairdressing salon just around the corner from the Post Office, which was very busy for the entire month of the initial showing. Some who did not need a haircut seemed to find an excuse to accumulate outside the salon window to see if they could spot themselves in the film.

The wallpaper on the walls of the row of cottages was peeled off by the film company quite soon afterwards. However, the grime smeared across the new slate roofs was left to wash away gradually with the rain, leaving mottled streaks down the previously attractive stone walls. The soldier's face atop the war memorial steadily reverted to its suitably sad and reverential former self, and the local people found new topics to discuss in the Post Office. Still, the village of Llanfechell was now famous!

Lynnette

27 Hay Days and Sad Days

"There will be a few farmers panicking right now," Philip said unexpectedly as we drove home through the back roads one warm summer Saturday after doing our shopping in Holyhead.

"Why is that?" I asked distractedly, putting away the shopping bill I had been perusing and rummaging amongst one of the shopping bags at my feet for biscuits to appease the hungry children in the back seats.

"Well, see that huge black cloud over there? Philip replied, gesturing towards the car window on my side. "There's a thunderstorm coming and not all of the hay has been brought in." Philip had worked as a young lad, helping with the hay baling for a farmer neighbouring his home in Hampshire and he clearly remembered how much work it took to bring in the hay quickly before the rain could come and ruin it.

"Look, there's a poor chap who looks like he could do with some help," he pointed out. Sure enough, just the other side of a stone wall, a man was working frantically, all by himself, tossing hay bales up onto the trailer attached to the back of his tractor. It looked like it was taking the last bit of his strength and there was much more to do to finish the job. We drove on a short distance, all feeling quite sorry for this man's dilemma, when suddenly Philip jammed on the brakes and reversed into the gateway.

"Sorry!" he said apologetically, being as we had all been thrown forward in our seats and were rather alarmed. "I can't just leave the man like that," he stated, pulling on the handbrake. "I won't be a moment." The name on the gate read *Rallt Goch* and the children and I watched from the car as Philip strode over to introduce himself to the farmer.

"Brian," the man replied, sitting briefly on a bale of hay and wiping his brow with his sleeve. "Sorry, I can't stop to talk at the moment, there's a storm coming, and I need to get all of this hay in." Then rising from his hay bale, he resumed his vigorous activity.

"Could you do with a hand?" Philip asked, and the man paused in his strenuous endeavour.

"I wouldn't say no," he replied, pleasantly surprised by this neighbourly offer.

"I will be back in twenty minutes," Philip said decisively as he hurriedly returned to the car.

"You don't mind if I come back and help that man with his hay, do you?" Philip asked, more as a statement than a question, as we sped off towards *Tŷ'n Llain* on the other side of the Mountain Road.

The dusty smell of ozone that descends with the first drops of rain, blended with the sweet fragrance of the dried vernal grass as Philip and Brian stacked the last few bales of hay into the barn. Philip enjoyed having the chance to use the pitchfork he had bought at the Amlwch farm closure auction; the ash wood shaft felt good in his hands, smooth and robust, with just the right amount of springiness. The rain began to hammer noisily on the corrugated iron roof of the barn as the two men stood under its

shelter, looking out at the strengthening tempest, relieved to have finished the job just in time.

"Let's go inside for a cup of tea," Brian suggested in his cheerful Cheshire accent and led the way as they ran quickly through the toy-strewn farmyard and into the old stone farmhouse. Children's artwork adorned the walls of the kitchen, while a black cat was curled up, purring blissfully in a basket next to the burning stove. Brian swept aside a scattering of breadcrumbs from the wooden table top, setting down two steaming cups of tea, with a couple of plates bearing thick slices of carrot cake.

"Petula and the children have gone over to sort out a few things at the hotel we are buying," Brian managed to say, between mouthfuls of much appreciated cake.

"You are buying a hotel?" Philip stopped eating momentarily to take in this information. "Where is that then?" he asked in surprise, since the evidence around him suggested that the family was settled happily there on the farm.

"The Gadlys," Brian replied, gathering up the last of the cake crumbs on his plate. "You must have noticed it."

"Yes, I know it," Philip confirmed. "Very grand looking place. Must be quite old?"

"Built around 1900 apparently, by a Brigadier-General Sir Owen Thomas," Brian elaborated, puffing out his chest and speaking in tones of mock self-importance. "It was a very popular luxury hotel in its hey-day, but right now it is quite sad and dilapidated. Now that the hay is in we can concentrate on renovating the hotel; we are hoping to have it ready for guests by the start of the next summer season." He smiled and sank back into the cushions on his wooden kitchen chair, relieved and replete. "You must come and visit us."

"We will!" Philip was delighted to accept and extended an invitation for Brian to bring his family across to visit us at *Tŷ'n Llain.*

It was a complete delight to meet Brian's wife, Petula with their two little ones when they called to see us some time later, bearing Carrot Cake. Petula was serene and softly spoken, with shoulder-length brown hair, while their six-year-old daughter, Anna was a shy miniature version of her mother. Four-year-old Peter was very timid at first and buried his little white-blond head in the folds of his Daddy's lumber jacket. However, after a bit of coaxing, our children managed to entice their young guests out to take some food to the pigs while we adults got to know each other.

The pigs were about six months old and getting to be a good size since they were managing to devour many sacks of leftover pizza crusts and spaghetti each week from our generous source in Bangor. They relished that food; their appreciation being evident by their total, noisy absorption in demolishing the entire supply in rapid time. They were also expert gardeners we noticed; they could roust a nice fat Dandelion root up out of the ground with ease in less than half a minute, just using their nose. What skill compared to how much effort it takes for us to extract a Dandelion root from the lawn with a trowel. We watched from the windows as the children and dogs explored the farm, with even Anna and little Peter getting into the spirit of adventure.

The minutes ticked by in the kitchen, with teacups and cake plates being replenished as we adults exchanged stories about our various backgrounds and experiences. However, what I thought to be particularly charming was the account of Brian and Petula's wedding day, seven years earlier.

"We did not invite many people," Brian began recounting the memories of that happy day. "To be honest, we couldn't afford a big wedding reception, so Petula's mother baked some cakes and we were just going to have a quiet cup of tea together after the ceremony."

"I wore a wedding dress my mother made for me," Petula added with a note of nostalgia, "and we all walked to the church through the country lanes together, gathering flowers from the hedgerows for my bouquet and headdress, while Brian and his best man found some for their buttonholes. My bridesmaid followed behind us, making her little posy from whatever flowers she could find." It all sounded so beautiful, and I could picture the scene, which was an anachronism in our modern world.

"When we arrived at the church," Brian continued, "we were amazed to see that the whole village had turned up for the service!" I could see memories of the happy experience dancing in his eyes as he expressed delight at the amount of support for their special day.

"My mother was so pleased to see everyone there that she invited all the villagers back to Carreglefn to share cakes and tea," Petula concluded, with a small tear forming in her eye. They smiled across the table at each other and it was evident that the magic of that happy day was still threaded throughout their marriage. They certainly had a tough job ahead of them with all they had taken on with restoring The Gadlys to its former glory, but we were sure that together they could do it.

We had often glimpsed that stately hotel on the hill, wondering about its history when we had passed it on the way to Amlwch. The name 'Brigadier-General Sir Owen Thomas' had been mentioned before in our hearing with mixed sentiments and we knew who would be able to fill us in on his details.

The following Sunday we had the opportunity to ask John Owen about The Gadlys Hotel when he arrived at the back door holding a long string of orange bailer twine, the other end of which was attached to our dog, Poppy.

"You will have to keep her under control, Philip," he warned. "The farmers around here don't take kindly to dogs who are allowed to run free across their land."

"Oh, thanks, John. Sorry about that," Philip replied, freeing the unremorseful vagrant from her bondage. "So, what have you been up to you little savage?" he addressed Poppy with as much severity as is useful in reprimanding a wilful little dog who has absolutely no idea what you are talking about. Poppy claimed innocence and pattered off to her food bowl to see if anything interesting had appeared there since she last looked.

"I know you look after your dogs, Philip, and they are not aggressive, but the farmers don't know that, neither do their sheep." John had evidently been thinking about how to alert us to the seriousness of the matter as he had meandered down across the top fields from Bryn Awel and he began to cite examples to drive his point home. We agreed that he was totally right, and that Poppy would need to be restrained.

"Come in and have a cup of tea with us, John," I offered, lifting one of the insulated hob covers on the Rayburn by its spiralled wire handle and sliding the kettle across to boil. The slumbering kettle burst instantly into activity on the hot plate with a few pops, bangs and rumbles and within seconds I was filling the teapot with its steaming water.

"Sheep worrying is a big problem for farmers," John pressed home his cause, nodding a smiling 'thank you' when I set his tea down on the table and added a large slice of ginger cake to the tea plate in front of him. "The dogs might think it a game, but the sheep can abort their lambs if they feel distressed!"

Philip grimaced at me as he took his tea and cake; I had to admit we had found it amusing to watch the small, black and white figure of Poppy, zigzagging happily across the fields on the scent of hares and rabbits. We could tell when she had seen one, for she would start to yap noisily as she scurried excitedly after it. Since stealth was hardly one of her better qualities, she had never yet managed to catch any and she would likely have no idea what to do with it if ever she did.

"You are right, John. We will keep her on a lead from now on," Philip promised, to assure him that he had taken the point. "Thanks for letting us know."

"John, we wanted to ask you what you know about The Gadlys Hotel and the man who built it," I ventured; "a Brigadier-General Sir Owen Thomas." John sat thoughtfully for a moment and then took a long draw on his tea. We knew that he was always pleased to share his extensive knowledge of local history, so we waited expectantly for his answer.

He explained that during the First World War, Brigadier-General Sir Owen Thomas was a high-ranking officer in the Welsh Guards. He was a politician and a very influential man; the building of the hotel being just one of the many achievements for which he is held in high regard locally. We were impressed to hear just how involved he had been in the development of the Cemaes Bay harbour and brickworks around the turn of the Twentieth Century and he was also among those responsible for establishing the Cemaes Bay Life-Saving Apparatus at Sea. We thought that Brian would be interested to hear what John had told us. However, there was a related piece of information from that time period that John commenced relating with passion.

"A quarter of a million young Welsh lads sent to the trenches, and too many of them never returned!" John stated fervently. "Having grown up being aware of so many missing men from his grandfather's generation, John could speak with authority on the matter. "The young men of Anglesey were good men, chapel men, they did not want to go to war," he continued sadly. "They would not have done so if they had not been coerced by those preachers who came into the villages, going around to the chapels, wearing soldier's uniforms with clergyman's 'dog collars' and telling them they could be expelled from the chapel if they did not do their patriotic duty!" John was speaking with the force of generations of resentment towards those who the locals felt had tricked them.

"Many count the 1918 Armistice as a victory, but for the people of Wales it was a very sad time when they realised how many of their men would not be coming home." It was evident from John's tone that he had been deeply touched by local history and the matter was still an emotive subject. He pointed out that all the war memorials in the towns and villages still bear the names of those men sacrificed on the altar of War, with Wales having particularly suffered an enormous loss of life. It had been a bitter blow for Anglesey, having lost around 4,000 of her members to the War effort and leaving a dearth of young men to meet the needs of the local young women, thereby causing many unspoken problems. Having recently lost his nephew, David Richard Williams, in the Falklands War and treasuring his own grown sons, the thought of those young lads being recruited into the army, only to die in the trenches of France, was understandably appalling to him!

John's anguished words occupied my mind over the next while and reminded me of my own family story.

My grandmother was only seventeen when the Great War broke out in 1914, later known as World War I. Laurie Amelia was the daughter of Arthur Lower, the local miller and his wife, Amelia. Nanny Laurie was the light of my life and that of my sisters, so we lived for the weekends when my mother would take us on the bus to visit her and our grandfather, Hector. Those Saturdays were the days that memories were made of; we learned so much about the life and experiences of our grandfather and the old-fashioned trades that he kept alive. We would often watch him mending shoes for the neighbours, using a hand-held, foot-shaped iron mould. Or we would peer over the rim of the kitchen table, hoping for tasters of sugar icing left over from the wedding cakes that he made and hand decorated.

As he worked, he told us about his life, during which he experienced the challenges and resulting damage of the two World Wars. For example, the frost-bite to his eyes, while stationed in Siberia, which caused him to now rely heavily on his thick pebble glasses. He related how he served as a chef on the ship, HMS Repulse, and reached the beautiful Islands of New Zealand. And he told of his grief for the loss of the sister ship to The Repulse, The Hood, which was sunk during the War along with her crew.

Hector Herbert Hearne in 1919 and Laurie Amelia Lower in 1923

During the evenings, while we waited for my father to come to collect us, we sat with our mother in the parlour around the warm, inviting open fire, listening attentively as our grandmother told us stories from her youth. The most poignant was the heart-rending account of her sweetheart, Leslie, who was one of the victims of World War I. He had been brought back badly injured to England from the trenches in France, and later died from his wounds.

Laurie was devastated! Leslie's family had never accepted her as his fiancé nor invited her to attend his funeral; however, she hid behind a tree in the cemetery and watched the grieving relatives surrounding the newly prepared grave. After the mourners departed, she slipped quietly from behind the tree and cast a red rose onto Leslie's grave, with the triumphant words: "They cannot take that away from me!"

Laurie later met and married our grandfather; a hard-working Berkshire man, who did his best to be a good husband and to heal her broken heart. It was not until after our grandmother's death however, that a small photo of Leslie was found amongst her personal affairs; it was enlightening to see the fresh-faced youth behind the sad tale. She had nurtured her grief throughout her adult life; another casualty of a terrible war.

28 Piggy Pandemonium

"Oh, aren't you beautiful!" Blanche, the relief post lady was instantly enamoured with our Poppy when she came to deliver the post. "What are you doing being tied up there then?"

"Poppy nearly got herself shot by the local farmers recently, so we have to keep her on a lead," Philip replied defensively as he opened the gate to the pen behind the old barn where he had spent his morning 'dagging' and 'crutching' the sheep.

"Oh, dear, have you been naughty, Poppy?" Blanche soothed, kneeling down next to her after handing Philip a couple of envelopes which looked ominously like bills of some sort. Poppy was an expert at giving the doe-eyed look of pathos and Blanche was thoroughly taken in. "She is very placid, isn't she?" Blanche commented. "You can never be sure with Jack Russells but she doesn't seem to be at all aggressive." Poppy played her 'Ace card' of persuasion and began to shiver and whimper as if she were cold and neglected, even though she had been well fed and it was a warm morning in August.

"Gentle as a lamb," Philip replied appropriately. "But she loves to go chasing rabbits on the neighbours' land and, as you can see, we have no way of keeping her under control here on the farm. We are afraid she will persuade our sheepdog Jill to go astray too, and then the pair of them would be in real trouble or even shot by a farmer!" Philip gestured toward Jill, who came forward to welcome our visitor with an enthusiastic wag of her tail at the mention of her name.

Blanche was aptly named; she was not a tall woman, but well formed, with thick white-blond hair cut into an attractive chin-length bob. She gave Jill a cursory pat on the head before returning her attention to Poppy.

"Aaw! Such a shame isn't it, Poppy, with all this land to explore?" she cooed indulgently. Deciding she had a collaborator, Poppy stretched out her front paws onto Blanche's knee and licked her hand affectionately. "No, you are very wise to keep her tied up," Blanche assured Philip, "I have heard of some sad stories on my rounds about dogs being shot as suspected 'sheep worriers'."

"So, I have been told," Philip said, recalling our interview with John Owen a few weeks earlier.

"I have a male 'Jack'," Blanche continued in an accent that Philip recognised as Southern English. "Perhaps you would like to meet him sometime, Poppy?"

'You don't know Poppy!' Philip thought to himself, remembering her aversion to the amorous advances of Sam and Toby the previous year. No, Poppy was a very self-possessed, self-willed young lady with a great sense of adventure and yes, it was a shame to have to keep her on her lead all the time, but the alternative was too dangerous.

Poppy began to look forwards to Blanche's visits, especially as she always came armed with a handful of doggie treats. She could hear the approaching little red van bearing the words *Post Brenhinol* long before it pulled up outside the house and she would skitter around the kitchen excitedly. We could be sure that

Poppy would not be going far all the time Blanche was coming to make a fuss of her, even if she had the opportunity.

"I think you need to come home with me, Poppy," Blanche said on another occasion, as she handed Philip an advertising leaflet. "No, seriously, if you ever decide to part with her, I have been considering finding a breeding partner for my Jackie."

"I will keep it in mind," Philip assured her. "But I think I would have mutiny on my hands if my children thought I planned to part with her." Within the week, Philip was to regret that decision.

They say there is a time for all good things to come to an end and the month of August meant that our pigs were well-fattened and ready to go to the butchers. We really did not want the children to be involved in the procedure; however, that situation became unavoidable. Pigs are intelligent animals, and ours were becoming rather suspicious when Philip backed the tractor and trailer up to their field gate.

"Here piggies!" he called out persuasively as he shook a bucket, half-filled with sheep pellets. Deciding they could manage without sheep pellets that day, the pigs trotted away to the far corner of the field. Opening the gate, Philip walked toward them, still shaking the bucket and calling out to them. "Come on, piggies, come and get your goodies." However, the pigs seemed to know that something sinister was going on and became thoroughly uncooperative. After following the little group around the perimeter of the field for several minutes, Philip decided it was time to call for reinforcements. Jill, who had been attempting to use 'mind control' on those disobedient creatures with her piercing amber stare, bounded onto the wall and over the wire fence at the first word of her master's command, and raced objectively toward them. Unlike sheep, however, pigs are not in the habit of being compliant with threats from a mere dog, and they stood their ground with stubborn resistance.

Daniel and Amelia arrived on the scene at that moment with Poppy on her lead, while Joshua followed close behind. All three children peered over the wall, watching the activity with rapt attention as Philip advanced toward the pigs. The closer he got, the further they moved away from him. Jill crouched down on the grass with her muzzle resting between her forelegs and her eyes riveted on the pigs. Gradually, the small group was being grudgingly persuaded in the direction of the gate, when suddenly Poppy decided this was all taking far too long. Breaking free from Daniel's control, she shot between the bars of the gate, yapping loudly. Although not in the least bit bothered by Jill's efforts to round them up, the pigs were shocked by the sudden intrusion of that little black and white menace and they scattered instantly to the far corners of the field.

"Poppy! Poppy! Come back!" the children all started calling.

"Poppy! Poppy! Go back!" Philip commanded crossly, but Poppy was on a mission and she was listening to no one. She dashed around the field, barking noisily and looking like she was having a great time, while the pigs cavorted heavily in all directions, squealing and grunting, with their large, floppy ears flapping wildly. Jill tried to no avail to round them up again, while Philip waved his shepherd's crook in an attempt to channel them towards the gate, with the hope that they would run straight into the waiting trailer. He had made an appointment with the butcher at Bodedern and time was running out.

With one last desperate attempt at disciplining those 'unruly' beasts, Jill made a lunge at the heels of one of them, which, with a deafening scream, headed straight for the gate, bursting its way through it. The other two pigs saw the opened escape route and the three of them lolloped at full speed out into the fields leading to the house, with Poppy, Philip, Jill and the children all chasing behind, shouting, waving or yapping in hot and raucous pursuit!

The sound of the approaching stampede caused Saffron and I to stop what we were doing in the kitchen and we looked at each other in bewilderment. It had not been the easiest of days; since she had started to crawl, little Saffron had discovered the delights of emptying all the cupboards in record time and now that she was gaining confidence, she was unstoppable. I found it hard to believe that this docile little madam, who had been content to lie or sit in her pram for the last ten months, happily playing with her toys or watching out of the kitchen window, should suddenly become such a whirlwind of destruction since she had become mobile! I was elbow deep in bread dough and had given up on refilling the cupboards with all she had emptied when she discovered a bottle of cooking oil with the lid not well-sealed. She thought it highly amusing to tip it all over the kitchen carpet and paddle in the resulting puddle. It was just then that we were both distracted by the strange noise from outside. Scraping as much dough as possible from my arms, I ran over to Saffron on the other side of the kitchen, grabbing a towel from the rail on the Rayburn as I passed it to wrap around her oily legs.

The noisy procession thundered past the front window in a blur of colour, then screeched its awful way around the side of the house and past the back door. I threw open the door with Saffron in my arms, just in time to see the stampede disappear around the far end of the house, before charging past the front window for a second time, then again past the back door. Standing in the middle of the kitchen together, Saffron and I watched as it did another two full circuits of the house, and then....silence! I decided it was time for Saffron's bath.

It was a hot afternoon, and the pigs were now panting heavily in the pen beside the old barn, into which Philip's unlikely *posse* had managed to drive them. Philip sat down on the low wall at the front of the house, while the dogs and children slumped, exhausted, onto the soft grass beside him. Poppy, her tongue lolling and her chest heaving with the exertion of her contribution to the vital task of pig discipline, gave Philip a wide doggy grin of self-satisfaction. Philip gave Poppy a hard stare of annoyance and the thought of Blanche's offer sounded very appealing at that moment!

Philip really wanted a long, cold beer, but it was getting late and time was pressing. Rising reluctantly from his seat on the wall, he walked around to the back door where the hosepipe was coiled around an old car wheel he had fixed to the wall of the house. He filled the water bowls outside the back door for the dogs, then dragged the hosepipe around to fill the water trough in the pen for the pigs and gave them a good cold shower to cool them down.

Saffron

By the time I arrived on the scene with a nice, clean Saffron and a tray of cold drinks for the pig herders, Philip had driven the tractor up from the pig field, unhitched the trailer and attached it to the back of the Volvo. He braced himself for the subsequent mission of getting the pigs into the trailer; but, they were far too exhausted for any further resistance. Resigning themselves to the inevitable, they walked with an air of defeat into the trailer and Philip closed its gate.

We only kept half a butchered pig, selling the rest to friends and family. However, it took us several weeks before we pulled out a piece of pork from the hidden depths of the freezer for dinner;

somehow, we did not have the heart or appetite for it. During the months that we had kept those pigs, we had become quite fond of them; they had distinct personalities and seemed far too smart, to end up the way they did. We decided against raising pigs for the pot again.

29 The Building Inspector

"Fascinating, isn't it?" I commented. Philip was also bemused by the scene when he came down from the fields to join me for a mid-morning *panad* on the bench outside the back door.

"How long has she been doing that?" he asked.

"Oh, for about the last twenty minutes, non-stop," I replied. "I didn't know dogs were capable of keeping that up for so long." Saffron, who I was nursing at the time, turned around at the sound of her Daddy's voice. "Ow! Saffron, be careful!" I winced. She had a good set of teeth at eleven months old, which sometimes made nursing a bit uncomfortable. I had breastfed all of our babies until they were at least a year old, or until they chose a banana over me and then I knew it was time for them to be weaned.

"Yes, she has been bouncing up and down like that since I put her washed bedding on the line," I explained, returning my attention to the amusing sight of Poppy attempting to retrieve her beloved blanket, which was flapping in the breeze on the washing line, tormentingly just out of reach. "So, do you want to see if it is dry yet, please? I think she will do herself an injury if she keeps that up for much longer."

"Come on, Poppy, let's put you out of your misery," Philip said soothingly as he unpegged the precious blanket, and laid it on the grass for her to lie on.

"We are going to miss her," I said sadly. "I just bathed her, so she is all clean and ready to go. The children were a bit tearful when they said goodbye to her this morning, weren't they?"

"Yes, it is tough on all of us," Philip replied morosely. "But I think they understood why she had to go and we promised we would take them to visit her at Blanche's home sometime soon, which cheered them up a bit." It was sad but necessary that Poppy should find a new home, for her own safety and that of Jill, who had been tempted on occasion to join Poppy in chasing rabbits over the neighbouring farms. We knew they were totally disinterested in 'sheep worrying', although the local farmers were understandably not so sure about that and one of them had threatened to shoot the dogs on sight the next time it happened.

"You know, it won't be long before *tupping* time," Philip said, dipping a biscuit into his tea and watching Poppy as she settled herself on her almost-dry blanket. "So, that means that in only another five months, the next batch of lambs will be due to arrive. I really want to have better control over the comfort of the next lambing season; lambing outside on cold, dark, and rainy nights is tough on the ewes, the lambs and on us."

"And?" I asked, wondering where we were going with this. It had been a pleasant summer break from school and the children had been keen to start the new school year, but I guessed Philip would now be ready to start on a new project.

"And I really think we need to build a multi-purpose barn," he tendered. "It would go nicely behind the sheep pen and overlook the field facing *Llyn Bwch*."

"Hmm...would you need to apply for planning permission?" I asked, although I knew Philip would find a way to build his barn regardless of the obstacles.

"No, not when the building is for agricultural purposes," he reassured me, and I knew then that it was as good as done.

The chosen site was relatively level, which was helpful; it just needed clearing of gorse, and dead leaves, and within a few inches of scraping, Philip revealed almost flat, solid bedrock. He hosed it clean and constructed a wooden shuttering frame, ready to lay the concrete base. Parys Mountain had been seeing renewed activity since the previous year and the mining company was now sinking the new shaft three hundred metres deep in the hope of finding copper, silver and maybe even a little gold. Philip was able to take advantage of the free offer of rock fragments dislodged by the drilling and blasting, with just the cost of the haulage to pay. With a home-made steel mesh screen, he was able to separate the hard core from the gravel-sized fraction, which, with some sand, cement and water, became the concrete foundation for the new barn.

Carl had recommended a good builder, Chris Chivers, and with Philip working as his labourer, they made rapid progress using concrete block construction. As he was working on a tight budget, Philip could not afford a steel lintel to go over the main door, so Chris suggested he build a brick archway instead. Perfect! Philip made a hardboard template for Chris to use and sourced some attractive red bricks to form the arch.

Shortly after moving into *Tŷ'n-Llain*, we were all pleased to discover that we had a resident barn owl. We had seen it on numerous occasions, especially on cold winter days, as it glided, quiet as a whisper across the land. Sometimes it would even swoop low beside us if we found ourselves outside as the evening began to descend. Philip wanted to encourage the owl's presence, so he asked Chris to build two owl holes into the wall above the barn door and set some of the red bricks as ledges for the

Saffron

bird to alight upon. Within two weeks, Chris had all four walls up, including gable ends and was at the point of constructing the roof timbers, when we received a visit from a man from Anglesey County Council, Llangefni.

He was a dapper little man, dressed in a khaki-coloured woollen jacket, crisp white shirt and steel grey trousers. He wore a dark moustache, slicked-back thinning hair, and a stern expression on his face. With clipboard in hand, the man perused the new building, walking around and inside it, tapping his pen against his clipboard and frowning. Declining the offer of a *panad*, he tutted and mumbled to himself while looking out towards *Llyn Bwch* and the surrounding countryside. Chris considered it wise to stop his work and, descending from the scaffolding, stood next to Philip to hear what the man had to say.

"We have received a complaint, Mr Barlow," the man finally said, tucking his clipboard away in his attaché case, "that you are building a chapel here." Chris and Philip were shocked; they thought the man must have been joking!

"Not at all!" Philip countered. "This is a barn; why ever would anyone think it was intended to be a chapel?"

"Well, what about those two crosses above the door then, Mr Barlow?" the man accused. "You are obliged to have planning permission to build a chapel, you know and that includes having the consent of your neighbours who share your access. They may not like to have a lot of people travelling up here every Sunday." Philip was stunned! Which of his neighbours would have been likely to lodge the complaint he wondered?

"Those are owl holes!" he burst out in irritation. "We have a barn owl who hunts this territory and we wanted to encourage it to make its home in the barn." The man did not look convinced by the explanation.

"No, I am sorry, Mr Barlow, but you must stop all further work until the matter has been fully discussed by Llangefni Council; you will receive a letter to that effect in a few days." He gave a cursory nod of farewell to the two workers, got into his car and drove off down the lane, leaving them staring open-mouthed at each other.

Sure enough, within a just few days, Blanche, the post lady arrived bearing a recorded delivery letter.

"Hope it is not bad news," Blanche said, noting the worried look on Philip's face.

"Hmm…me too," he replied; although he had a good idea what the letter contained, he preferred to delay opening it. "So how is our Poppy doing, Blanche?" Philip asked with feigned nonchalance.

"She's just fine," Blanche brightened at the mention of the recently-added member to her household. "Taken over the place already; poor Jackie has definitely found himself displaced from being 'King Pin'!"

"That sounds like Poppy," Philip chuckled. "We are so pleased she has gone to a good home where she will be safe and well cared for."

"She will earn her keep you can be sure of that; Jackie adores her, even though she has claimed his favourite chair," Blanche responded with a cheeky smile as she climbed back into her little red post van. "Oh, by the way, this is my last week on the post-round," she added, just before closing the van door. "I am being made redundant now that the regular postman is ready to come back to work after his operation."

"Well, I am pleased to hear that our postie has recovered," Philip replied sympathetically, although he was duly concerned for Blanche. "But what will you do for work?"

"Oh, I don't know," she answered sadly, with her usually bright and cheerful countenance overshadowed by an evidently heavy heart. "There is not likely to be any other work for me; I will just

229

have to sign on for unemployment benefit again, I suppose."

Philip stood on the driveway, watching as the post van bobbed and rocked its way back down the bumpy lane. He felt sorry for Blanche, she really enjoyed her work and he knew how depressing it was to be unemployed, despite one's best efforts to avoid that dismal situation. He then returned his gaze to the unwelcome letter in his hand.

30 The Best Interview Ever!

Philip had been driving each Thursday for some weeks to the Mobile Job Centre, which was a caravan, parked in the central car park in Amlwch. It was a well-organised effort by the local government, bringing a glimmer of hope and encouragement to the unemployed. The staff members were sympathetic, kind and helpful, providing newspapers, trade journals, telephones, stationery and a photocopier. Posted on a notice board were a few rare local job opportunities, but in the main, the advertised employment was for work in the large cities of England. Most of the jobs offered were in Finance, Law and Information Technology (Computing), an industry in its infancy at that time. Philip had been sending off at least four job applications a week, but with no success and very rarely even a reply, which was very disheartening. The 1980s were difficult times for tradespeople right across the British Isles, since no longer was a willingness to work hard a guarantee of having a job.

On one of those Thursdays in the springtime, Philip decided to lift his spirits by walking over the top fields and following the footpaths to Amlwch, about six miles 'as the crow flies', for his weekly visit to the Mobile Job Centre. The morning was sunny, with barely a breeze, not cold but cool, crisp and fresh. It was so quiet that he could only hear the bleating of ewes and lambs calling to each other as he reached the boundary wall separating the top fields of *Tŷ'n Llain* from those of our neighbour's farm, the *Coeden*. Climbing the stile over the dry-stone boundary wall, he realised he needed to take care to follow his detailed Ordinance Survey map closely, to trace the rarely-used path in search of the next stile and the many others en-route for Amlwch.

One of the many things we came to appreciate about Anglesey

231

is that, as it has such a long history of human habitation, there is a well-established, jealously protected network of footpaths, which weave like a cobweb across the whole Island. From his point of elevation, Philip could look right across to Parys Mountain, where the pithead winding gear was quite visible, indicating that the recent activity on the mountain was continuing. Perhaps with interest from the new investors, this could mean employment for hopeful locals? Striding across the *Coeden's* fields, Philip was impressed by the way Wyn Rogers cared for his land; it was impeccable with well-fertilised, lush green pasture and contented, well-nourished livestock. He felt even more motivated to find work to have the funds to give our fields the treatment of which they were seriously in need. Yes, lime and fertilisers were the key issues, but that required money.

There were few footpath signs along the route Philip wanted to take and only a line on the map he was following. Therefore, it was with relief that he eventually found himself at the next stile, leading onto the Carreglefn Road. He had only a few hundred yards to walk along that quiet country lane while looking for the continuation of the footpath and sure enough, he discovered a small gap in the tall, dense hawthorn hedge, which all but hid the little iron gate he had hoped to find. A step through that gate, and it was like going into a different world.

The descending slope became steeper until it reached a sheltered glen of oaks and sycamores, which clustered around the ivy-covered remains of a small, stone-built house, and derelict, water-powered *Pandy*, or Fuller's mill. A pair of Jackdaws, in the process of constructing a nest atop one of the oaks, voiced harsh complaint at Philip's intrusion. Moss clung to the base of the tree trunks like soft green cushions, while the banks of the little brook, which ran alongside the mill and trickled off down the valley, was decorated with clumps of vibrant daffodils. Philip took a few moments to think about the history of the little house, which must once have been a family home and cottage industry. The Fuller would have used the power of the stream for cleaning and beating the raw sheep's fleece until it became a waterproof felt. He tried to imagine the little family that had once lived there; a family like ours, perhaps? He thought of the children who would have run barefoot along the banks of the stream, splashing happily in its waters and who had probably worked beside their hard-working parents to learn their valuable trade. Now though, their beloved home was little more than a tumbledown shell.

Crossing the brook, using a tiny bridge and climbing over a wooden stile, Philip left that precious scene behind him. After a few hundred yards, some wooden steps got him over the next boundary wall, then down onto another country lane. Taking a few moments to orientate himself, he consulted the map again.

"What to look for next?" he asked himself aloud. "A dovecot? What kind of a landmark is that?" Ahead, he noticed a picturesque stone-built tower, about forty feet high; it was well maintained, having a good slate roof, and a door at the bottom, but there were no windows, only holes in the top with little ledges. Evidently, this was the dovecot and his cue to exit the country lane and head across the fields again. It seemed to Philip that not all farmers upheld the country rules on keeping the walkways clear and accessible, as he searched the dry-stone walls edging the road for the next gate or stile. He was considering the need to clamber over the barbed wire-topped wall when he eventually came to a somewhat rusty farm gate, which swung open noisily, threatening to drop off its hinges.

Closing the gate carefully behind him, Philip again consulted the map. About a mile in the distance was his next clearly defined target, a small wooded area atop a gentle rise. In the middle of the field, he was surprised to encounter an enormous standing stone that rose erect and dagger-like from the ground, about twenty feet tall, six feet wide, and around eighteen inches thick. Philip felt a chill go through him at the sinister sight, feeling uneasy at the thought of what this stone may have been used for in ancient times. Druid human sacrifices perhaps? That may have explained why the farmer had not made the walkway easily accessible, with this ancient relic being so vulnerable to any possible abuse.

Walking a few times around the stone and wondering about its history, he noticed the immense, incongruous sight of the, grey/green oil storage tanks of Shell Rhosgoch Oil Terminal, just about half a mile away. What a contrast between ancient and modern! There was a distinct eeriness about the area, so quickening his pace, he walked swiftly up the rise and around the back of the woods. There was not a bird to be heard, not even the sound of wind in the trees; it was as quiet as the proverbial graveyard.

Stepping sleeper to sleeper along the tracks of a railway line running down to Amlwch, Philip noticed that the top of the steel rails had a light coating of rust, indicating that the railway line was rarely used. Perhaps it was only employed by the weekly goods train, which carried the poisonous Methyl Bromide liquid from The Associated Octel works next to Amlwch Port. The product was extracted and concentrated from the pristine seawater and was an essential additive to petrol in the days before unleaded petrol was available. He was pleased to finally reach the Job Centre caravan and partake of a well-deserved cup of tea. A young man of about twenty-five sat in the corner of the caravan and Philip greeted him with a cheerful "Good morning." When the man returned his greeting, Philip could tell that he was English and very nervous.

"*Bore da*, Mr Barlow." The familiar voice of Mrs Wyn-Jones, the manageress of the Centre, called out from a partitioned room inside the caravan. "You will need to be quick with that cup of tea as I have an appointment for you in just fifteen minutes." Philip was pleasantly surprised, almost shocked; however, somewhat muddied from his journey, he expressed concern that he did not feel dressed for a job interview.

"There's no need to worry about that, Mr Barlow," the manageress assured him as she emerged from behind her partition. "We have heard from a company wanting to hire local workers immediately for the demolition of the Rhosgoch oil tanks and they need someone like you who has had experience using a gas torch to cut metal." This was the best opportunity Philip had had in all the weeks of visiting the Job Centre! Although he felt instantly encouraged and hopeful, he also felt a twinge of uneasiness at the prospect of filling in any forms or applications under the watchful eye of his potential employer. Form-filling had been his nightmare for as long as he could remember; he could not understand why he had always had such a problem with writing when most other people did not seem to struggle as he did. The difficulties of conveying thoughts to paper had plagued him throughout his school life, leading to exasperation on the part of his teachers and persecution from the other children.

"Are you ready, Mr Kersey?" Mrs Wyn-Jones asked the young man in the corner who began gathering up his paperwork and rucksack at her authoritative, but kindly command and followed obediently to the waiting vehicle. Ian Kersey had qualified as a skilled welder before recently coming to live on Anglesey, Philip learned, as the three of them sped along the road in the direction of Cemaes Bay. The sky started to darken, and specks of rain began to pepper the windscreen.

"This interview will be with Ogden Demolitions Ltd. gentlemen; they have been contracted to dismantle the oil tanks and remove all the metal from the site." Mrs Wyn-Jones politely interrupted the conversation between her two hopeful clients and continued to impart vital information to assist them in finding favour with their possible future employer. Philip recalled that we had not seen the gigantic crude oil carrier ships passing the mouth of Cemaes Bay and mooring off Bull Bay for at least six months; now he understood the reason for that. 'So, Shell Oil is pulling out of Anglesey, which will mean more jobs lost,' he reflected despondently.

The enormous steel oil tanks, eighty or ninety feet high, loomed up before them as they turned off the main highway and onto the well-made private road. They passed two large, old cranes with derricks mounted on caterpillar tracks, which were being prepared with maximum extension booms needed to reach up above the tanks. There was a smaller crane, also on caterpillar tracks, fitted with a giant-sized electromagnet for loading low-grade pieces of scrap metal into high-sided lorries. The car turned into a small compound of 'portacabins' and parked alongside the site agent's office, from within which emitted the sound of a very loud, one-sided conversation, filled with demands and expletives.

"Perhaps we should wait here for a little while," suggested Mrs

Wyn-Jones tactfully and the men were more than happy to comply. The conversation inside the office ended abruptly with the thud of the telephone being slammed down, and then almost immediately the cabin door swung open.

"Ah, Mussuz Wyn-Jones," the site agent's face melted into a congenial, welcoming smile as he strode towards our chauffeuse and gently grasped her hand in both of his muscular mauls. Patrick Kenny was a powerful, stocky man, possibly in his mid-fifties, about five feet eight inches tall, with a dense, unruly mop of red-tinged, sandy-brown hair, which he frequently swept back from his pale, freckled face. He had a thick, Southern Irish accent and a bulbous red nose, indicating he was a heavy drinker.

"Good morning, Mr Kenny," Mrs Wyn-Jones returned his greeting demurely before graciously presenting her wards. "I have Mr Kersey and Mr Barlow here to see you today." Patrick Kenny slowly turned his attention from Mrs Wyn-Jones, and his fiery, blue-green eyes hooded over menacingly as he set them upon the timid candidates while his smiling countenance 'morphed' into a fear-inspiring, stormy expression.

"So, you two jokers think you can cut metal, do you?" he demanded.

"Yes, Sir," Ian ventured as he proffered his dossier rather shakily toward Mr Kenny, who glanced disdainfully at it without taking it from him.

"And what makes you think you are up for the job?" he demanded of Philip, who squared up to the man, meeting his threatening stare unflinchingly. He had suffered enough mistreatment at school to know a bully when he met one and he was not prepared to be subjected to such behaviour now, as a grown man.

"I can do this job!" Philip stated. "I have had experience in cutting steel with oxy-acetylene gas while working in the cement works under extremely difficult conditions, with heat from the kilns and noise from the ball-mills. Also, I have qualified as Banksman/slinger to work with the crane drivers, which I think could be useful to you." A faint smile creased the corners of Patrick Kenny's eyes and Philip could tell he had won the man's respect.

"There is a tight time schedule; this contract must be completed by mid-August," Patrick Kenny stated. "Therefore, if it rains, you work in the rain or whatever else the weather throws at you; the work does not stop, but you will be provided with protective clothing." By then, the light drizzle was becoming increasingly heavier, giving suitable background effect to his words. Mrs Wyn-Jones decided it was time to retire to her car to do some paperwork, while Patrick Kenny continued spelling out the ground rules of the job.

"The steel tanks have a thick coat of lead paint, meaning you will wear a respirator at all times, no matter how hot it gets and you will submit to a blood test every six weeks, starting from week one. Slackers will be dismissed!" Torturous threats continued to drop like daggers from his lips, but Philip felt that his previous experiences had prepared him for the terms so far.

Just then, however, the 'bomb dropped'!

"The two cranes you see over there; one will have a lifting beam with chains and clamps for holding the steel sheets as you cut them. The other will have a two-man cradle and you will be in that cradle!" Mr Kenny stated mercilessly. Now that prospect Philip considered the worst of all the rules of this 'assault course' since he had an extreme aversion to heights.

"You will be provided with cutting equipment, which will include packs of sixteen oxygen bottles, a coupled pack of two propane bottles and long hoses," Mr Kenny continued in his efforts to evoke fear into the hearts of his victims. "There will be a cutting torch and you will be given just one, eighth-of-an-inch diameter nozzle per week. If you burn it out and come back to ask for a second one, you will be instantly dismissed because you are no good at your job!" Patrick Kenny leaned toward the men intimidatingly, scanning their faces for any trace of fear or reluctance.

"Forty-five hours a week, three pounds an hour," he stated, after a few moments. "Do you still want the job?" Philip had very little time to reflect on this offer; it was evident that the work would be hard and the pay low. However, he was keenly aware of his responsibility to provide for his family, a privilege that he would never relinquish. Having no alternative offers of employment so far, he decided to accept.

The rain was torrential and the wind fierce when the children and I drove to the home of Paul and Candy in Amlwch that evening to collect Philip. He was already there, playing cards and enjoying a cup of tea with them beside their warm, inviting open fire and he was exuberant.

"The best job interview ever!" he announced with a beaming face. "Not a single form to fill in and I start work on Monday."

31 Rhosgoch Arena

The rain and wind continued over the weekend and on into the following week. By seven o'clock that Monday morning, Philip had reported for work at the Rhosgoch site and Ian was also there, standing nervously to attention. Although justifiably apprehensive after ruminating all weekend on the strict requirements and punishing circumstances threatened by his new boss, Philip was eager to get started. The first thing required was a blood test to check their starting lead levels, which was done by an efficient, but good-natured doctor from Cheshire, who wore the oversized tortoiseshell-rimmed glasses fashionable at the time.

"I am what you might call a 'mobile vampire', if you like," the man said with a toothy smile, as he strapped the tourniquet around Philip's upper arm. Philip guessed that this procedure was done more to cover the company against future claims than for the benefit of the workers. Next was a visit to the site storeman, who was a man of medium height, slight build and nearing retirement age. He addressed his job with proficiency, as though preparing the two men more for space travel than for work on a wet and windy Anglesey day!

"You will need to shave off that beard so the mask will fit properly to protect you from lead poisoning," he stated bluntly. Philip was very attached to his beard, so he was in no hurry to relinquish it if he could avoid doing so.

"How about waiting until we have the results from the next blood test to see if the lead levels have increased? If they have, then so be it, I will shave off the beard," he suggested hopefully.

"Aye, but you will need to keep the mask on all the time you are working mind," the storeman cautioned Philip sagely, wagging a bony finger at him to stress the importance of his warning. He turned and rummaged amongst the shelves and boxes in the

241

depths of his porta cabin, re-emerging with two multi-coloured boiler suits made from oddly shaped material remnants. It seemed to Philip that the boiler suits were not expected to last very long with the rough treatment they would receive, which added to his mounting sense of foreboding. Kitted out with their bizarre boiler suits, black steel-toe-capped boots, bottle green plastic hard hats, gaudy orange goggles with dark green lenses and 'superhero' welders' gauntlets, made from thick, rust-red suede, Philip felt they could have passed for circus clowns, instead of tough guys with a mission!

The storeman strapped a battery-driven respirator to each of their backs, with an electric motor, an individual filter canister, specifically for blocking lead fumes, and a flexible rubber hose to link the facemask to the backpack. He then produced the thirty-inch-long gas torch cutting equipment from his store with the valuable fluted brass nozzles, which would mean instant dismissal if they burned out within the week.

Out in the yard, two outsized, heavy crates awaited them, one for each man and each containing sixteen big black oxygen bottles. Accompanying each pack were two extra-large, orange-coloured propane gas bottles linked with a brass regulator and loaded onto a four-wheel-drive forklift truck, ready to be brought out to the worksite. The truck driver was an elf of a man named Kevin, who proudly sported a thatch of black hair, a neat moustache, and pointed beard and a constant smile as he went merrily about his work. At this point, Mr Kenny, the site manager, emerged from his office, wearing a white hard hat and a black donkey jacket with orange, high visibility shoulders. He looked the two men up and down and gave a smile-less nod of satisfaction at seeing his new workers all suitably equipped and ready for action. With the wind and rain in their faces, the three of them set off for the massive tanks.

"Trefor! Trefor!" Mr Kenny leaned into the roughly cutaway opening in the side of one of the tanks and shouted to a man working inside. Trefor Jones emerged from the depths of the tank, part-harlequin, part-astronaut, in his kaleidoscopic working gear and removed one red suede gauntlet as he reached out to shake hands with Philip and Ian. Trefor looked like a man in his fifties, with a firm jaw and a warm, friendly smile.

"Trefor, these two jokers are starting work today, so I want you to show them the ropes." Patrick Kenny jerked his head commandingly at his two new workers and smiled at Trefor, in place of a please or thank you. Pulling his coat collar up around his ears and plunging his hands deep into his pockets, Mr Kenny turned and marched hurriedly back to the warmth of his smoky office.

"So you have had experience with gas cutting, have you?" Trefor asked, and both men nodded affirmatively in answer to his question. "Then, you had better connect up your torches." Philip realised he could have made himself look a complete fool if he had forgotten that the gas connections are opposite-thread or anti-clockwise, compared to oxygen, which has a clockwise-thread with a blue hose for the oxygen and a red hose for the gas.

"Now, we cut with oxygen and propane gas; it is not as good as oxy-acetylene, but it is much cheaper," Trefor informed them before leading the way into the tank. Philip and Ian hauled the long, heavy, coiled hoses onto their shoulders as instructed and followed him through the cutaway opening, laying out the hoses behind them as they went. The intimidating sensation of stepping into a gladiatorial arena hit them as they entered the tank, which seemed to have its own distinct, evil-tempered weather system. The wind and rain swirled in a fierce, gusting spiral, pushing, shoving, knocking and tugging at the men like an unseen foe bent on forcing them to lose their balance and stumble to their knees.

The lid to the tank was an enormous, perfectly fitting steel pontoon designed to float, rising and falling with the oil level to keep it sealed safely below. However, since the last of the oil had been pumped away to Ellesmere Port in Cheshire, the lid sat on the floor of the empty tank, covered in rainy puddles. The steel was only suitable for scrap metal, so their task was to cut it into manageable 5'x2' rectangles, which could best be achieved by standing on it and cutting it beneath their feet. Igniting the torch with the flint tinder was easy enough; however, Philip found it extremely difficult to hold it steady against the buffeting of the wind. Keeping the flame just above the metal and heating a spot the size of a sixpence until it was white-hot, he pressed the thumb lever sending a blast of pure oxygen onto the super-heated steel, which burst into a spectacular plume of colourful sparks and flares. Once the steel started to burn, it became a self-sustaining furnace, provided he could keep the blast of oxygen steady and constant. That was no easy feat, as the wind seemed to have taken savage personal delight in confounding his efforts. While cutting the metal through the puddles, he felt like a lobster boiled, feet first in hot water. Sparks flew, the water boiled, steam hissed and rose as the pools drained away. The rain poured down, and the wind howled around his ears, but Philip was pleased to be working and earning a wage.

"*Ynys Dawel*; yes, it sounds like you have seen *Ynys Dawel!*" Trefor Davies answered Philip's question the following day in hushed tones as the two men stood on the road outside the tank in which they had just been working. Trefor glanced over his shoulder to make sure they were alone before continuing.

"Yes, it is a mysterious place that is only known to the locals by its old Welsh name, meaning 'Quiet Island'"

"Well, it certainly was quiet; strangely quiet!" Philip concurred, raptly interested in finding out more about the little wood and the standing stone he had stumbled across on his walk to Amlwch the previous week.

"Yes, the birds don't sing there," Trefor continued as they walked toward the tearoom together for their mid-morning break.

"That's it!" Philip agreed. "That is exactly it! There were trees but no bird song!"

"Tradition has it that it was a prehistoric battlefield; the human blood shed on that field has made it a sacred site, which may be why the standing stone was placed there," Trefor explained. "Another possibility is that it could be there to mark *Gorsedd Wygyr*, meaning Throne of *Afon Wygyr*, or the source of the river that comes out in Cemaes Bay. We believe that river springs were considered sacred to my ancestors, the ancient Celts." The conversation was fascinating, and Philip learned so much in that walk between the oil tanks. However, both men fell silent as they reached the tearoom and noticed the empty space in the car park where young Ian had parked his car that morning.

"Rotten job! Rotten working conditions! Only three pounds an hour!" Philip recalled Ian's retort to Trefor's advice after they heard the nozzle on Ian's torch pop, hiss, and die that morning. "I don't care if I do get the sack!" Ian had said, throwing down his equipment in frustration and marching back towards the site agent's office. And now he was gone, and it was only his second day at work.

"I warned him not to go back and ask for another nozzle," Trefor said, shaking his head in disappointment as he stared out through the window of the tea room, his mug of tea in one hand and an enormous sandwich in the other. "I told him he could have borrowed one of my old ones; I clean my nozzles regularly and keep them as spares when we get the new one each week, just in case." Philip, who had already finished his tea and sandwich, immediately pulled out his nozzle from his pocket and started to file and clean it, just as Trefor had shown him.

Loud-Mouthed Larry, Philip privately named the man quite soon after he had started work, and for a good reason. Larry was a Yorkshire man, possibly in his late forties, with a ring of long, wispy brown hair but bald on top, a circumstance that only revealed itself when he removed his helmet. He was very lean, a heavy drinker, a heavy smoker, and argumentative about everything, his voice usually being heard over those of everyone else in the tearoom. He created arguments, and he always won them. On this particular day, Philip was the assigned Banksman, responsible for directing the crane drivers using legitimately recognised hand and arm signals, much like Semaphore. He had the daunting task of ensuring the safety of the workers, both on the ground and high above it. Larry and a fellow Yorkshire man named Tom dangled high above the ground in the cradle, which hung from the hook of one of the cranes. They had just cut out a large, heavy sheet of steel from the side of one of the tanks, now held by the second crane, using a lifting beam and jamb cleats.

Dafydd Jones, the driver of the second crane holding the steel sheet, was disadvantaged as he could not see clearly due to the obstruction of the other crane; therefore, he needed to rely heavily on instructions from the Banksman. However, ever wanting to be in control, Larry was not prepared to wait quietly while Dafydd and Philip coordinated their efforts to lower the sheet safely to the ground. Larry bellowed directions and diatribes from his lofty position, Dafydd Jones became flustered and confused, causing both crane booms to collide, and almost spilling out Larry and Tom from the cradle. The steel sheet broke free from its clamps and plummeted eighty feet to the ground, as swift and deadly as a guillotine blade! It sliced off two thick steel brackets, welded to the side of the tank and embedded itself upright in the tarmac, just inches from the crane cab that carried Larry and Tom in its cradle. The driver was shocked and shaken, but not nearly as much as Larry and Tom; they clung desperately to the sides of the cradle, which swung as violently as a conker on a schoolboy's string until it eventually stabilised, and they were lowered to the ground where they were able to stagger out. After that experience, Larry was silent ... for at least five minutes.

On another occasion, it was Larry's turn to be Banksman while Philip and Trefor were very high up in the cradle. Part of Larry's responsibility was to position the crane so an entire sheet could be cut without moving its caterpillar tracks. However, the men were halfway through a cut, but the crane could not stretch far enough to complete the task.

"Hold on tight; we are going to move the crane," Larry's authoritative voice called up to Philip and Trefor. They obeyed immediately, although with little confidence, as the sturdy old Ruston Bucyrus crane began to rumble forwards on its 'clackety-clack' caterpillar tracks. Larry was standing in front of the crane, beckoning it towards him when the front end of the caterpillar tracks suddenly found soft, wet ground and sank about twelve inches. Larry leapt to the side as the crane boom plunged toward

him, missing him by inches, while up above, Philip and Trefor in the cradle felt themselves free-fall for a good ten feet before coming to a jolting halt and then bouncing wildly as if on a string of elastic!

Everyone involved was in shock, and as the men climbed shakily from the lowered cradle, they noticed that Larry looked decidedly white and in stunned silence. Ever practical, Trefor declared a break and a soothing cup of tea while the crane was repositioned onto safe, firm ground. Larry sat at the back of the tearoom, sipping his tea without uttering a word.

It was a bitterly cold day just a few weeks later, with a harsh wind, which left one chilled to the bone or 'starved', to use a Yorkshire expression. Philip wore his old duffle coat with synthetic fur lining while working high up in the cradle with Trefor. Sparks and molten metal beads flew in all directions, and as Philip and Trefor concentrated on cutting out the large sheets of steel, they chose to ignore the shouts from Larry on the ground below them.

'That man always has something to shout about,' Philip thought. The shouts intensified, however, so Trefor leaned over the railings of the cradle and looked down to see Larry, who was waving his arms wildly in unofficial signings and pointing at Philip. Trefor turned to see what Larry was pointing at and saw that Philip's duffle coat was aflame with red/black sooty smoke! Trefor and Philip worked quickly to remove the blazing garment, thrusting it out from the cradle, where it glided gently downward in a mass of flames.

For once, Philip was grateful for Loud-mouthed Larry's input and for living up to his nickname!

32 Sheeting in the Mizzen!

Philip was beaming as he proudly presented me with his first wage packet, as if he had been holding the crown jewels. It was a fat brown envelope, bulging with twenty-pound notes; I was genuinely amazed, I had never seen so much money in one packet. The payslip said £3 an hour as agreed, however, although he had only worked for 45 hours, Philip was paid for 155 hours, which amounted to £465! I was shocked!

"How did you...? What happened...? Why ...?" I did not expect that, and neither did Philip. He was suitably pleased by the effect his surprise had on me and proceeded to relate his own reaction when he was given his wage packet:

"Are you complaining?" Mr Kenny had asked when Philip knocked on his office door to point out the apparent error.

"No, Sir," Philip had replied.

"Then neither am I," Mr Kenny had stated with an unexpectedly benevolent, warm smile gracing his rugged face. It was the nearest to an accolade that Philip had yet received for his hard work and endurance. The following week and every week after that he earned the same amount, plus productivity bonuses on top of that. Philip thought of poor Ian Kersey who had not stayed the course and who could have benefited from the same reward as himself.

"We could put down a deposit on another vehicle so you can take the children to school or perhaps I could borrow one.... I will talk with your Dad; maybe he can come up with something." Philip's words were music to my ears. My parents had been so helpful, driving up and down from Cemaes Bay to take the children to school and back each day, but the situation was not ideal. The following Sunday evening the telephone rang; it was PJ, my sister Terrie's husband, phoning from Kent. My father had contacted him and told him of the good news about Philip finding work and the need for additional transport.

"Would you like to borrow my motorbike for the summer, Philip?" PJ offered. He was more than a brother-in-law to us, he was also our dear friend, he and Terrie having shared a double wedding with us, twelve years earlier. We had lived in the same village after getting married, our children were the same ages and, despite the miles that now separated us, our lives were woven inextricably in a lifelong bond of friendship.

Philip and PJ were very different personalities and from very different backgrounds. Philip, a serious and cautious Hampshire country lad and PJ, the cheeky, mischievous Londoner, always ready to laugh at himself and to be the 'clown' who kept us all entertained. In their youth they had ridden their motorbikes together, exhibiting their riding skills as young men do. However, Philip knew that PJ was the 'Master'; he rode in complete harmony with his bike as though he were a part of it, soaring, twisting, turning and taking the bendy roads with the ease and grace of a swallow in the air. Philip felt it would be a great honour to be entrusted with the use of his brother-in-law's treasured motorbike.

"Where are the children?" Philip asked, noticing their absence after work the following Friday evening.

"They are still with Mum and Dad," I replied distractedly, "they should be here soon."

"I really need to put some of our money into greening up the fields," Philip announced as he stood at the kitchen sink eyeing the brown terrain, which was a stark contrast to the fertile green fields of our neighbours. I had just poured him a cup of tea when we heard the sound of a motorbike coming up the driveway. PJ, on his glossy black Suzuki GT 550 motorbike rode cautiously up to the house, avoiding the boulders and potholes on the uneven driveway.

'Crackle, crackle, crackle, pop, pop, pop, pop, pop, stop!'

Off-road riding was not his forté and his superb bike was far too precious to lose to a rut or a ditch on our driveway. Philip strode out through the back door to meet his dear friend who dismounted, stretched and removed his shiny black helmet. The two men were delighted to meet up and hugged each other warmly.

"Rough old driveway, Philip!" PJ exclaimed, the corners of his eyes creasing with that familiar cheeky grin we knew so well. "I nearly came off once or twice."

"Yes, sorry about that, PJ; the rain has washed away a lot of the gravel this week," Philip replied.

"Terrie will be bringing the children up from your Mum and Dad's soon," explained PJ, giving me a big bear hug. Saffron shyly buried her little blond curly head in my chest when he kissed her on the cheek. Philip was delighted when PJ pulled out a bottle of whisky from a bag tucked inside his black leather jacket. "Well, we have something to celebrate!" PJ exclaimed.

And celebrate that weekend we did! It was an opportunity for belated celebrations of our shared wedding anniversaries, with Paul, Candy and their children joining in the happy event, along with Paul and Terrie's children, Kirk and Crystal. We had a thoroughly enjoyable weekend, spent mostly at my parent's home, eating our mother's renowned Sunday roast dinner, with large and fluffy Yorkshire puddings, filled with meat gravy and with whipped cream-topped trifle for dessert. Mum's home-made wine flowed freely (for those who were permitted to imbibe), while 'Acker Bilk' played softly in the background and all the cousins ran happily together around the house and garden. Our children had a lot of respect and affection for 'The Aunties', and always looked forwards to their visits, for they usually came bearing gifts and CHOCOLATE, and this visit was no exception.

After dinner, Terrie suggested that Philip take her and Paul for a trip around the bay in his Drascombe Lugger sailing boat, which he kept permanently moored there in the harbour. Philip was sceptical though, for the wind was quite strong that day.

"Look at the water; it's flat." Terrie pointed out as we all looked out through the large picture window at the sparkling blue waters of the bay.

"Yes, but look at the sky," Philip countered. "There is a south-westerly storm coming from across the Island; the bay may be calm, but the sea will be rough beyond that."

"But it would make such a nice finish to a lovely weekend," Terrie implored, in her most appealing and persuasive way.

"Right then, are we ready?" Philip's crew were all clad in their life jackets, keen and eager to go. "You know what to do, don't you?" Philip asked, as PJ took his place at the tiller, ready to steer the boat. He had been out on Philip's previous boats on the Medway River, so he felt quite confident in his assignment.

"Terrie, would you please hold on tightly to this rope? And when I give you the word, you have to quickly pull it tight and tuck it into the cleat here on the side of the boat." Philip demonstrated his instructions as he spoke, and Terrie confirmed that she understood what was expected of her.

As it was so windy, Philip decided to hoist just the foresail and the rear mizzen sail, leaving the mainsail safely furled. The boat sped instantly from its moorings as its brick-red coloured sails caught the strong offshore wind. Terrie was enthralled, her lovely face a picture of excitement as she waved at we spectators who were leaning over the sea wall, cheering our sailors on encouragingly. Travelling at right angles on a 'broad-reach' to the wind, the little boat skipped lightly and quickly across the bay, narrowly missing a small fishing boat chugging into the safety of the harbour from the turbulent waters of the Irish Sea. PJ gripped the tiller, beaming with delight as the responsive vessel yielded to his control. Terrie, with her blond hair whipping around her face, looked as though she was enjoying the experience immensely and started pointing towards the mouth of the bay. Philip shook his head and wagged a finger of negativity in her direction; he was mindful of a tragic event our friend Ernie the plumber had related to us, that had happened not long before we arrived on Anglesey.

A group of local young people had been kayaking in the harbour one summer's day and had decided to venture out beyond the mouth of the bay. Neil, the son of our friend, Ernie the plumber, had been among the group, but had obeyed his Father's strong warnings about the dangers of the savage tidal races in those waters, so instead of joining his friends, he had turned homeward. Sadly, neither those young people who had ignored the warnings, nor their kayaks, were ever seen again, despite frantic coastal searches by teams of friends, family, locals and the Cemaes Bay Coastguard. The mystery and grief surrounding the disappearance of those young people still hung like a sinister pall over the Island.

Unaware of that tragic tale, Terrie was still nodding and pointing hopefully. Hence, the intrepid trio ventured further out from the shelter of the inner bay, but still within the 'safe' waters of the outer harbour. Staying close and running parallel to the cliffs, the little boat kept on a steady, even keel, while most of the wind howled overhead, creating dangerous waves only a few hundred yards further out to sea.

Knowing the deadly reputation of that coast, Philip was becoming increasingly anxious when Wylfa Power station loomed up on the clifftop above them and the murderous rocky islets of *Ynysoedd y Moelrhoniaid* or the Skerries, off Carmel Head, appeared to be creeping uncomfortably close. Philip decided they had gone far enough, and it was time to head back to safety; it was at that point however, that the wind began to strengthen. PJ battled unsuccessfully with the tiller, while the sails flapped wildly, and the loose ropes flogged and whipped from side to side!

"Sheet in the Mizzen, Terrie! Sheet in the Mizzen!" Philip shouted as he attempted to regain control of the rear sail, forgetting in his panic that she was not familiar with nautical terms.

"What?" Terrie shouted back, alarm etched on her face as she clung to her rope as previously instructed, but she had no idea what Philip meant.

"Sheet in the Mizzen, Terrie! Quick!" Philip repeated his command while Terrie looked around for a clue as to what she was supposed to do. The boat lurched violently, threatening to spill everyone into the water, and Philip feared that it was in danger of being scooped up and hurled toward the raging sea. He leapt from his seat, grabbed the rope from Terrie's hand, rammed it firmly into the jamb cleat and pulled it tight. The wind then caught the mizzen sail from behind and the boat swung obediently back toward the harbour, with its occupants clinging to its sides in various stages of shock or relief! It had been a short, fast and exhilarating excursion, but everyone was pleased to be heading back towards safety.

"Sheeting in the Mizzen?" Terrie quizzed Philip, repeating her version of his words when the crisis was over.

"Yes, sorry; that was a nautical term, not a swear word," Philip assured her. "But you got the point, didn't you?"

"I certainly did!" Terrie said with feeling, the colour beginning to return to her face. "More than I care to confess to!"

Lynnette

33 Stuck on the Rocks

It was one of those rare, beautiful summer days with not a breath of wind, and all was peaceful on the farm. The lambs frolicked together across the emerald green fields like a mini-stampede, while their mothers grazed contentedly in the warmth of the afternoon sunshine. The Rayburn was lit, ready to heat the water for hot baths in the evening and a casserole was cooking slowly in the oven. I bundled little Saffron into the car, eagerly seizing the opportunity to drive to my parents' home in Cemaes Bay, where together my mother and I walked the dogs, Lucy and Cassie up through the village to meet the children from school.

The walk back through the village was always a pleasant one and that day it was alive with contented villagers, also enjoying the warmth and sunshine. Melodious Welsh chatter mingled with the excited squeals of children running home from school, keen to splash in the gentle, cooling waves in the harbour. Elderly men politely dipped the peaks of their well-worn flat caps, their faces weathered and scored as evidence of many years of seaside living. Their lady counterparts, with obligatory headscarves tied tightly over silvering hair, concurred with gracious nods and smiles as they battled to contain their creaking wicker shopping baskets, loaded with tissue-wrapped, fresh-baked bread and locally grown vegetables. They squeezed into the shop doorways edging the narrow pathway to allow us to pass with Saffron in her pushchair, smiling indulgently at Daniel and Amelia, as they struggled to control the two exuberant dogs, eager for their daily run on the beach.

Joshua bounced from foot to foot, attempting to avoid the cracks between the paving slabs, his energy unbounded despite his busy day at school. Our route took us past the bakery, the air a-waft with the tempting smells of *Bara Brith* and freshly baked bread.

Passing the Doctor's surgery, we lingered in front of the popular grocery store, where brightly coloured displays of tin buckets and spades hung in clusters alongside the doorway. Distracted briefly from his pavement game, Joshua gazed longingly at the array before him; his big blue eyes sparkling with delight under his thick blond fringe.

We cautiously navigated the crossing of the road that leads to Amlwch, where a bridge spans a deep wooded ravine, through which flows the *Afon Wygyr* and where several small boats nestled among the trees below. The *Ffordd y Traeth* (Beach Road) that we followed dipped and wound its way between whitewashed stone cottages perching on the water's edge on one side and the Stag hotel with its colourful flower baskets on the other. Behind the stone-walled front garden of the hotel, contented clientele occupied the salt-bleached wooden furniture, clutching tall, foaming glasses of chilled beer as they basked comfortably in the welcome warmth.

The children raced ahead, and the dogs, released from their leads, bounded over the harbour wall and romped delightedly in the coarse white sand, sending startled seagulls screeching in noisy protest as they took to the air. Suddenly Daniel came running back toward us, his eyes flashing with excitement and his chestnut curls bouncing across his forehead as he pointed to the clifftop on the opposite side of the bay.

"Mum, Mum, look; I think that is Debbie, and she is screaming!" My mother and I quickened our pace and shaded our eyes against the glare of the afternoon sun to make out the form of an agitated child jumping up and down on the cliff's edge. Several feet beneath her, a man seemed to be clinging to the rocky cliff face.

"Do you think he is just stuck and can't manage to climb up to the top of the cliff?" I asked as the children climbed onto the low stone sea wall to get a better view. The man certainly appeared to be in some difficulty, for he kept reaching up to his full height and then dejectedly squatting down again on a grassy tussock that jutted out from the cliff face All the while, the girl on the clifftop was screaming and calling out for help.

"Perhaps he has broken his leg," my mother suggested.

"Perhaps we should call the coast guard," I replied, in the manner of the 'Royal We', and meaning that she should do it. After a quick run on the beach to regather the dogs, the children chased excitedly up to my parents' bedroom where they knew they would find their grandfather and they regaled him with the exciting drama. Since retiring from his double-glazing business, my father loved just to sit in his rocking chair, watching the waves coming in and out of the bay.

"And how is our baby doing?" he asked fondly, as I greeted him with a kiss on his forehead.

"Coming on," I replied, proudly displaying my swelling belly. "He is almost four months now," I stated, as I deposited Saffron on his knee. I was convinced that our baby would be a boy; boy, girl, boy, girl, boy. That was the way it had gone so far; apart from that I was keeping very healthy and was carrying him very well, as I had the two boys.

"It's all right, they are on their way to help," my mother announced, and proceeded to give a detailed report of the telephone conversation she had just had with the local coast guard as she joined us at the bedroom window where a clear view of the cliffs on the far side of the bay could be seen.

"Look! Look! Uncle James is up on the top of the cliff now!" exclaimed Amelia, excitedly pushing aside the tartan-patterned ribbon, which had grown limp and ineffective after a day of holding back a lock of her silky blond hair. Sure enough, the man stuck on the rocks, who could have been our friend, James, was now atop the cliff, and several black-clad figures had joined him. The coast guard thanked my mother for her second phone call to inform him that the reported problem appeared to have been resolved.

"However, all reports must be responded to and the initial call will continue to be acted on," was the official reply.

"Oh, well, it is good to see there are people who care, isn't it?" my mother commented pragmatically to the little watchmen at the window. "How about a nice cup of tea?" Joshua, having pre-empted her suggestion, had already appeared with the biscuit barrel; it had been a busy day for a little boy and his school dinner had long since ceased to give any comfort to his rumbling tummy. A loud bang and a flash of orange light over the bay distracted our merry band of biscuit munchers and they all rushed back to the window to investigate.

"Someone must be in trouble out at sea," my mother suggested.

"Maybe the coast guard will be too busy dealing with that to concern himself with some man who we thought was stuck on the rocks," I offered hopefully, feeling rather silly for stirring up unnecessary drama.

Philip had also noticed the smoke trail of a rocket, terminating in a loud, explosive 'boom!', as he approached Cemaes Bay on his way home from work that evening. He mentioned it over dinner, reminding the children of the exciting events in the bay, which they proceeded to relate to their father enthusiastically.

"The children seem to think it could have been James who was stuck on the rocks; do you think it might have been?" Philip asked as we cleared away the dinner plates and prepared his lunch box for the following day.

"We must ask him next time we see him," I suggested with reservation.

A few days later, we had the opportunity to do just that when James, his wife Sharon and their two young daughters, arrived unexpectedly to share a *panad* with us.

"Was that you stuck on the rocks last week, James?" Philip asked as I filled the teacups and encouraged everyone to help themselves to sticky chocolate cake. The eyes of all the children were upon James, in anticipation of his answer. Ignoring the teacup in front of him and the offer of cake, James sank his head into his hands and let out an audible groan.

"Oh no, don't remind me," he replied.

"Were you hurt?" I questioned him anxiously, peering under the table to see if, in my haste to be hospitable, I had not noticed any broken limbs or plaster cast. Daniel, Amelia and Joshua followed suit, but James was too absorbed in his own issues to notice several children suddenly disappearing under the tablecloth. Their bewildered faces reappeared at the sound of the chocolate cake being served and James decided, with appropriate interjections from Sharon and the girls, to enlighten us on the afternoon's events from *their* side of the bay.

James and Sharon had collected their girls from Cemaes School on that beautifully warm and sunny day and had gone straight to the beach. They aimed to walk along the headland, across the cliff tops, passing Llanbadrig church and on to *Porth Padrig* Beach or White Lady Bay. To add more adventure to the occasion, James and Debbie were going to be 'intrepid explorers', attempting to rock-climb their way up to the top of the cliff, while Sharon and Madeline took the more sedate cliff path.

"I managed to push Debbie up the last few feet of the climb, but there was no foothold for me to be able to make it up to the top myself," James continued his account. As our children had reported, eight-year-old Debbie had panicked and was calling frantically to her mother for help.

"Debbie, Debbie, I'm alright! Stop panicking!" James had called out to her, but she would not be appeased.

"Mummy, Mummy, where are you? Daddy's stuck on the rocks!" Debbie had cried out, reaching an almost frenzied state.

"Whatever is the matter?" her mother had replied, red-faced and panting as she hurried to the top of the steep cliff path toward her distressed daughter.

"Daddy can't climb up the cliff!" Debbie had exclaimed and the colour that had flushed Sharon's face with the exertion of her brisk walk, then drained with the alarm inspired by her daughter's announcement.

"James, are you alright?" Sharon had winced with pain as she stretched out on her hands and knees to peer over the nettle-strewn cliff top.

"Yes, I am fine, but please tell Debbie to calm down!" James's retort at least reassured her that he had not plunged to his death on the jagged rocks at the base of the cliff, where the shallow blue water washed gently around the ankles of a cluster of squealing, happy children.

"Well, what happened? Did you slip down?" His wife entreated.

"Of course, I didn't!" James had replied testily. "I just can't pull myself up these last few feet; there are no footholds. Look, I managed to push Debbie up and I could be up there myself if I had something to hold on to," he explained, stretching up to his full capacity to demonstrate his dilemma, but his fingers still came just short of the clifftop. "Hey, pass me down your bag strap, and tie the other end to a gorse root or something, then I will be able to climb up." James' face had lightened with that flash of inspiration.

"Definitely not! It's my new one and you might break it!" his wife had retorted indignantly, clutching her handbag to her breast. She and her daughter shared the same strong sense of dramatics, thought James, as he entertained a fleeting vision of the new bag strap breaking and of himself plummeting to the rocks below where the group of children were now pointing at the funny man who seemed to be stuck on the rocks.

"I don't know why you insisted on climbing up this way with Debbie anyway," Sharon continued. At the mention of her youngest daughter, she swung around to check on her whereabouts and was relieved to see she was merrily swinging on a nearby field gate. Her elder sister Madeline, tired from the long trek up the cliff path, was sitting on a grassy mound, wholly focused on making daisy chains. Sharon raised herself from her uncomfortable position and edged back toward safety. "I'll see if I can find a piece of rope up here," her disembodied voice wafted down to James.

"No, don't worry, Sharon; I will climb back down the way I came," he said, looking around him to see if that could be an option.

"You can't do that!" Sharon's shocked face reappeared instantly, behind a flurry of wind-tossed hair; "all those people will laugh at us!" she said, pointing toward the beach below, where several small groups had now gathered. The squealing amongst the children had subsided somewhat as James' predicament began to attract attention. James had then dropped his hands from groping at the gravelly cliff face and slumped into a defeated crouch. Meanwhile, Sharon was examining a tangle of kite string that nine-year-old Madeline had discovered in a gorse bush and the two of them became deeply engrossed in untangling it to be of some help. James gave a reassuring wave to his audience below as he viewed the tranquil scene, taking in the entertaining theatre of summer activities that can only happen at the seaside.

A small blue fishing boat drifted steadily along the horizon, disappearing behind the grass-topped cliffs at the mouth of the outer bay where the steep grey walls of Wylfa Nuclear Power Station glinted like a beacon in the sunlight. On his side of the bay, small children laughed delightedly, holding up their buckets for the lugworms the adults were digging up in readiness for the fishing that would take place from the harbour wall later that evening. A group of children and a couple of dogs frolicked on the strip of sandy beach on the opposite side the bay, while behind them a medley of squat, white cottages, as picturesque as stage scenery, tumbled down toward the beach. A pleasant chiming sound drifted up from the harbour as the halliards struck the metal masts of the sailing boats, which rocked from side to side while being gently lifted with the rising of the incoming tide. Some elderly men leaning over the harbour wall had paused in their conversation and, holding up gnarled, wrinkled hands to shade eyes a blue-wash with Time, peered through the bright afternoon sunshine at the man who looked as though he was stuck on the rocks.

"Will you be wanting some help there?" James was just beginning to enjoy the peacefulness of the moment, despite his predicament, when suddenly a man's voice with a strong Irish accent called down from the clifftop above.

"Oh, thanks," James had replied gratefully, as the man let down some durable cable for him to hold on to. Grasping it firmly, he scrambled to the clifftop, ignoring the resulting pain caused by the nettles. The Irishman had beamed a warm smile in answer to the profuse thanks from James and his family before sauntering happily along the grassy track leading down to the beach. However, he was soon apprehended by a group of men hurrying purposefully up the track. The Irishman turned and pointed to James and Sharon, who, with a wave of consternation, noticed that the burley group was now marching meaningfully towards them.

"Are you the man stuck on the rocks?" the group leader demanded unceremoniously. Under his black woollen hat, his large, round face glowed red and steaming from his strenuous exercise and from the weight of the heavy rope wrapped diagonally across his torso. His companions, similarly attired in unseasonable weatherproof jackets and sturdy walking boots, came to a halt behind him, all breathing heavily and glaring at James with the same irritated air.

"No, I was not stuck on the rocks; I just could not climb the last bit until that kind man helped me up just now," James had hoped to make light of the situation as he gestured toward the Irishman in the distance. Silence reigned as the faces of the men grew steadily dark and menacing.

"But I am OK now, as you can see," James had added, wondering how those aggressive individuals had managed to get involved in his dilemma. The hefty ringleader was not interested in the details but demanded to know why he had called them out if he had not been in danger. James tried to explain that he had not asked for help and assured the man that he had no idea who had asked them to come to his rescue. With that, the lead man exploded with expressions that more than adequately informed him of the extreme effort put into his rescue by the entire Cemaes Bay Rescue Team!

Just then a rocket with a distress flare had soared into the air, bursting noisily across the blue sky, turning it a bright orange-red. James hoped to benefit from the distraction and slip out of the limelight.

"Looks like someone else is in trouble!" he had ventured as the sky began to fill with the sound of a helicopter speeding in from RAF Valley. From somewhere in the distance he heard the wailing of an approaching ambulance, mingled with the undulating sirens of ensuing police cars.

"No, all of this is for you!" growled the lead man, who stood motionless and frowning, his feet planted widely and his arms akimbo in a show of aggravation and accusation. James was shocked and speechless as the awful truth of his role in this *Comedy of Errors* in which he starred suddenly dawned on him.

"Now, will you please accompany us back to the Coast Guard's office to explain yourself?" the angry man commanded, before stamping back along the cliff path with his seething support team muttering together irritably in his wake. By the time James, Sharon and the girls had reached the car park on the beach, a large crowd of beachgoers was milling around excitedly, waiting to see the man who had caused so much commotion. Egged on by the leader from the rescue team, the crowd was threatening to become a daunting lynch mob! James had bravely attempted to rise to the occasion, climbing onto a boulder, holding up his hand and smiling unconvincingly like a good politician, according to Sharon.

"Thank you, everyone!" he called out across the confused and milling multitude. "Thank you; it's all right, it was a mistake. I was not stuck on the rocks, just in a little difficulty but I am fine now. Thank you, thank you all." James waved graciously as he was led past everyone to the waiting ambulance to sign the necessary discharge forms. He then thanked the policemen standing, unamused and scowling at him beside their gleaming, white police cars. Sharon and the girls seized the opportunity to slip away quietly to the family vehicle, from where they could watch in anonymity as James was marched up to the Coast Guard's office on the road overlooking the bay. An assortment of bemused and inquisitive holidaymakers lined the route, watching intently as though he were being led to the gallows.

Reaching the top of the stone-walled steps, his heart sank to see the entire Cemaes Bay Rescue team collected around the entrance to the Coast Guard's office. Mustering an extra dose of courage, James pushed through the well-equipped, disgruntled volunteers, to sign what he had hoped would be his last form and to make his final apologies. After being given a stern warning never again to cause the people of Cemaes Bay such inconvenience, James was dismissed and had once again to brave his way through the discontented assembly of rescue workers waiting outside.

"Thank you, everyone; thank you, and I am so sorry to have disturbed you all. I was not stuck on the rocks, but it is so good to know you are here if we need you," James called out. However, despite his patronizing efforts, the muttering, and growling amongst the group intensified, so he considered it wise to make his way swiftly across the road to the stone steps, leading back down to the beach and to his waiting family. James was relieved to see that the crowd that had flanked his course on his ascent had lost interest and dwindled, except for one elderly man who was making arduous efforts to climb the steps to discover the cause of all the fuss. The man stood wheezing at the top of the steps, clinging to the wall for support as he gasped for breath.

"What is going on here?" he eventually managed to ask.

"Oh, nothing much," James replied, looking furtively over his shoulder at the irritated mêlée behind him. "Some idiot managed to get himself stuck on the rocks!"

The group sitting around our kitchen table dissolved into hysterics as James finished his story and our children started poking Debbie and teasing her over her part in the episode. Philip was in such contortions that he almost spilt his tea, while Saffron joined in the occasion, squealing loudly as she sat in her highchair, rubbing chocolate cake generously over her face and into her curly blond hair.

"That must have been very stressful for you, James," I acknowledged, hoping that none of my family would give away the secret of my involvement in the event.

"Yes, I'll say!" James replied as he took a well-deserved swill of his tea. "But I tell you, I would love to find out who it was that sent out that distress call!" He shook his head woefully as he reached for his slice of chocolate cake.

The kitchen fell almost silent except for the giggles of Debbie and Madeline, and the bubbling of the kettle on the stove, while a host of blue eyes stared expectantly at me in anticipation of my reply. I thought for a few seconds about how I might form an adequate, honest confession. Then, taking a deep breath and looking at James directly, I said what clearly needed to be said:

"More tea, James?"

34 Blazing Inferno

The contract at Rhosgoch was well along and nearing completion. The tanks were all dismantled, leaving only the pipework and the pump house to deal with. Mr Kenny had been true to his word and had laid-off workers as the project neared completion, keeping his hardest workers until last. Philip and Trefor Jones were among those remaining, as was Dai Thomas, a South Walian, and, despite his annoying ways, so was Larry.

The pair of three-foot diameter oil transport pipes, which were a remarkable feat of engineering, ran below ground from Northwest Anglesey, across the Island, under the muddy sands of the northern Menai Straits, up and over two mountain ranges, and ending up at the Stanlow Oil Refinery, Merseyside. When in use, those pipes were cleaned by a 'pig', an ingenious device slightly smaller than the diameter of the pipes and encircled by stiff wire brushes. The pig, named because of the squealing sound it made while travelling through the pipeline; was inserted regularly into the pig launcher, and the pressure of the outgoing oil would push it all the way through, scouring the interior as it went. Now those redundant pipes were to be capped and protected in the ground, just in case they could be of future use, and it was time to cut up the pumping station. The pipes immediately before that point had never been cleaned, and despite using the strongest pressure washers, the thick, waxy oil deposits inside them would not shift. As time was too short to bring in specialist cold-cutting equipment, Larry was assigned to cut up the pipes using oxy-propane gas. However, because of the fire risks involved, he flatly refused to do it!

Mr Kenny called Philip into his office.

"Philip, I have a little job for you," he said in his most winning manner.

Philip soon found himself completely kitted out with a white asbestos suit, incorporating a piped, forced cold air supply, helmet, gloves and boots, ready to take up the challenge. Mr Kenny, Trefor, Dai and the other men watched as Larry attached a wire rope to Philip's belt so he could be dragged out of danger if necessary, while Trefor had a foam-generating fire hose at the ready.

Philip stepped slowly and nervously toward his assigned task; he struck the flint, ignited the gas and, after tuning the oxygen to give a bright blue flame, he started by cutting the flange bolts. After a few minutes, the flange separated, and the massive, curved steel pipe fell to the ground with a thud. So far, so good! Through his narrow visor, Philip could see his support team several yards away, nodding and encouraging him, but the only sound he could hear was his own heavy breathing.

Next, he had to cut the pipe into quarters; he heated a small spot of metal on the side of the pipe until it was white-hot before blasting it with a jet of pure oxygen. The thick layer of waxy oil ignited and instantly engulfed him in flames! Oblivious of the dramatic effect he was having on the watching men from whom he was hidden within that blazing inferno, Philip continued to work on, systematically cutting up the metal.

The other workers gathered in an anxious cluster as Philip slowly emerged, unscathed, from amongst the billowing orange and red flames and clouds of black smoke. A warm, broad smile broke out on Trefor's face, and Dai looked thoroughly relieved. Mr Kenny clapped a large hand of congratulations on the back of Philip's scorched and smoking outfit, while Larry was shocked and speechless. The foaming fire hose doused the flames around the pieces of pipe, and the job was done!

By the end of the following week, the tea room had been dismantled, leaving only the portable offices, the storehouse and a few remnants of metal to be disposed of or collected. The cranes and their drivers were dispatched to Barrow-In-Furness in the North-west of England, ready for the next project for Ogden Demolitions, along with most of the remaining demolition workers.

"Well done, Trefor! Well done, Philip!" Patrick Kenny was not known for giving commendation, but he seemed to be making an exception as the project had finally come to an end. He was the image of warm congeniality, a side of him that Philip had not seen in all the months he had known him.

"Trefor will be travelling with the company to the next job, Philip; how about you?" Mr Kenny asked. "You are a hard worker, so I would like to make you the offer of joining the team and travelling with us as a permanent employee. What do you think?" Philip looked down at the thick wage packet in his hand and the envelope containing an unexpected, substantial bonus.

He could tell that Trefor, who was watching him closely, was hopeful he would accept the offer as they had become good friends over their time working together.

Trefor   Dai   Philip

"You have earned good money during your time here, Philip; you could continue to send it back to your family each week from here on," Mr Kenny continued persuasively. The wage packet in Philip's hands felt weighty, and he had to admit that the prospects of financial security and the opportunity to earn like this every week sounded very tempting. He thought of the fields of *Tŷ'n Llain*, which were greening up nicely now he could afford to fertilise them; of how Lynnette could buy beautiful clothes and special treats for the children and would not need to 'penny pinch' with the shopping. He took a deep breath, and his eyes met those of Mr Kenny.

"Thank you, Mr Kenny," he said decisively. "I really appreciate your offer, and I have been grateful to you for giving me this job, but my family means everything to me, and I would not dream of leaving them." Patrick Kenny's eyes searched Philip's face, and his hard exterior melted into a smile of approval as he laid his hand meaningfully on Philip's shoulder.

"I think you have made the right choice, Philip," he said with conviction, and Philip felt he had seen a brief glimpse of the real, feeling man behind the façade, a man who perhaps wished he had made the same decision decades earlier. "So, what do you think you will do now, Philip?" The hard man reappeared suddenly, regaining control as the gruff employer.

"I have seen an advertisement in the local paper from the Welsh Development Agency offering 'City and Guilds' courses for the unemployed, so I think I will follow up on that." Philip was pleased to be able to give a positive reply. Patrick Kenny nodded thoughtfully, and Trefor uttered a few words of encouragement. "But in the meantime," Philip brightened, "I hope to finish building my barn before winter, and I just wondered if those steel beams left on the site were going spare?" Mr Kenny shrugged his shoulders and turned to walk back to his office.

"Take what you like," he said over his shoulder; "it will all be going to the local scrap dealer after today." Stopping at the door to his office, he turned and gave Philip a smile and a wave of farewell. "Best wishes to you, Philip!" Mr Kenny added sincerely before closing the door.

"*Wela i chi* (See you later), Philip," Trefor Jones shook Philip's hand warmly as a sad 'Goodbye'.

"*Wela i chi,* Trefor," Philip replied, but they knew they were not likely to see each other ever again.

35 Dancing with the Devil

"Three hundred guineas. Three hundred and fifty. Four hundred. Four hundred and fifty? Four hundred and fifty! Five hundred!" Philip stared in disbelief as the bidding rose rapidly for the proud ram paraded around the auction ring. "Seven hundred. Seven hundred and fifty. Seven hundred and eighty. Eight hundred! Any advance on eight hundred? Eight hundred and ten? Eight hundred and ten. Eight hundred and twenty? Sold for eight hundred and ten guineas!" The auctioneer's gavel came down swiftly on its block, meaning that John Owen had successfully bid on behalf of his client for what Philip decided to be the ugliest beast he had ever seen!

The Blue Faced Leicester is not known for its beauty at the best of times, but this one he thought had to be bordering on grotesque! A gigantic beast, looking like an oversized ball of shaggy wool, balanced on two pairs of knitting needles as he trotted confidently around the arena for a final bow. His long, bare neck stood erect, at right angles to his body, and his angular head, covered in short, white hairs, was topped with spiky 'rabbit ears', which looked almost like horns. His bulging amber eyes peered out menacingly from dark grey settings, and his oversized Roman nose, curved into an evil-looking, toothy grin.

"Well done, John; that was excellent! Good work!" Steve Williams was delighted with the purchase that John had helped him to make and gave him a friendly slap on the back in congratulations.

"Yes, well done, John; well done, Steve," Philip concurred He had met Steve for the first time just before the start of the auction while unloading our ram from the back of John's pick-up truck ready for sale. Steve was of Welsh origin, he had grown up in England but was now returning to his roots on Anglesey and John had been doing some fencing for him on the farm he had recently bought on top of the cliffs overlooking Cemaes Bay.

"I don't suppose there is any chance of my ram fetching anything near that price," Philip lamented as the auction continued. Caesar was in a deplorable condition, and any offers the auctioneer could muster for him would be a bonus. In exchange for future grazing rights, Philip had bought the small flock of pedigree Suffolk sheep for the asking price of £80 each from our neighbours, Roy and Millicent from *Hafod Las*. Sadly, their fields had succumbed to an infestation of *battus worm;* therefore, Sally, the vet, had advised getting the sheep quickly onto clean pasture. The six ewes were rallying nicely, but poor Caesar was not doing at all well. His emaciated body had been eaten away from within, so his strong black head looked disproportionately large and cumbersome. His unsteady gait gave evidence of the extent of his unhealthy condition as he was led into the ring, where a murmur of scorn, pity, or mirth rippled throughout the audience.

"So, what am I bid for this purebred Suffolk ram, with pedigree papers?" the auctioneer proposed derisively as the bidders began to quieten down. He made an unsuccessful effort to conceal his amusement, and the laughter started again. John and Steve glanced sympathetically at Philip, who sank into an embarrassed hunch on the wooden bench, hoping no one would connect him with the pathetic creature at the centre of attention. "Eighty guineas," the auctioneer continued. "Who will give me eighty guineas? Seventy? Who will give me seventy guineas? Sixty?" The farmers on the benches flanking the arena were still smirking and sniggering, and Philip was losing all hopes of going home with anywhere near eight hundred guineas for his sick ram.

"Come on now, gentlemen," the auctioneer attempted to muster some response from the gathering. "Fifty guineas? Forty? Gareth, what can you offer?" All eyes turned toward the 'Grim

Reaper' from the knacker's yard, leaning against a rail to one side of the room with his arms folded and with an air of quiet confidence. Chewing on a piece of straw, with his flat cap shading astute eyes, while watching the proceedings, he awaited his opportunity for a good deal.

"Five guineas!" he called out with a sinister smile and continued chewing on his piece of straw.

"Five guineas! Am I offered ten? Ten guineas?" The auctioneer was trying his best on Philip's behalf. "Come on now, Gareth, ten guineas?" Gareth nodded, and the auctioneer brought his gavel down hard on its block before the man could change his mind. "Ten guineas! Sold, for ten guineas!" shouted the auctioneer, and poor Caesar limped away pitiably to the back of the arena.

"If he had spent less time doing his job and more time eating good grass, he might have been as healthy as his ewes," Philip stated as he and John drove back towards Cemaes Bay in John's pick-up truck on that warm afternoon in August. He was understandably disappointed by the outcome of the auction and very sad for the inglorious end for his once glorious ram.

"But hopefully, he will have left you with some fine lambs, Philip," John replied, doing his best to raise his spirits.

"Oh, yes, he managed to cover all his ewes, and most of them could be bearing twins. I think I will sell them as pregnant ewes, and they will surely be worth a lot more than poor old Caesar," Philip responded. "Why was Steve prepared to pay so much for this ugly beast?" he asked, gesturing toward the back of the truck, where Steve's new purchase was travelling on his way to his new home.

"Ah, now there is a good question, Philip," John said, glancing sideways at him, pleased to be able to impart information on one of his favourite topics. "The Blue Faced Leicester put to the Welsh

Mountain ewes will produce 'Welsh Mules'; bigger than their mothers, but with the same hardiness and excellent motherly instinct of the Welsh Mountain sheep. Steve will keep back all the female lambs, and when they are mature, he can run the Suffolk or Texel *tup* with them. He will then have good-sized ewes, easy lambing, with big lambs fetching top price, and he can rent out his expensive ram to other farmers to cover their sheep too." John's eyes glittered with pride at his achievement, and Philip guessed that John would also benefit from his support for Steve that day.

"I suppose then that in just one or two more years, Steve will easily get a good return on what he paid for that beastie and more, although he did have the devil of a job getting him to cooperate when he tried to get him into your truck. I can see trouble ahead for him!" Philip warned.

"Yes, it looks as though he has a wicked temper, that ram; powerful too! I hope Steve can manage him," John agreed and sat quiet and thoughtful for a few minutes. He then started humming a happy Welsh ballad as they drove along the quiet country roads to deliver Rufus the ram to Park Lodge farm.

Two weeks later, on a fine summer day, John Owen slipped through the farm gate next to Jeffrey's field and strode in his unmistakable jaunty manner toward our house. Only a light breeze disturbed the sweet, fresh air that day, so we ate our lunch at the picnic table by the back door. The children were always pleased to see John, whom they viewed as a benefactor since he had given them the television, so they squeezed up to make a space for him to share a *panad* with us.

"I have terrible news for you, Philip," John announced after exchanging the necessary pleasantries. All eyes were upon him to hear what horror story he was about to tell. "That ram Steve bought at the auction, you know? Well, I was working for him on the sheep handling pens at his farm when the ram charged at Steve and broke his thigh bone!" A gasp broke out around the table.

"No! Surely not!" Philip was open-mouthed and shocked by the news.

"It is true, Philip," John confirmed, taking his place on the edge of the bench and accepting a large mug of tea with a gracious nod in my direction. "And, you said you thought he would be trouble, didn't you?" Philip rubbed at his beard thoughtfully, shaking his head in disbelief that the evil-looking monster could have been so aggressive.

"Well, yes, I did, but I did not think he would be that bad!" he replied. "How is Steve?"

"Not good! Not good, Philip. Plastered almost up to the hip, and they say he will be out of action for some months," John related sadly before taking a gulp of tea. "The trouble is, he needs to dip his sheep next week, and he has arranged for Sally, the vet, to come and trim their hooves at the same time."

"Well, he will not be able to manage that from the sounds of it," Philip stated.

"Not at all; not at all," John agreed. "That is what I wanted to ask you, Philip; I will be going to lend a hand, and I wondered if you would come and help too?" The children were all listening with rapt interest to the conversation; they were already familiar with the account of the costly 'great ugly beast' Philip had related when he returned home from the auction.

"I will come with you, Dad; I can help," eleven-year-old Daniel piped up eagerly.

The last of the summer visitors were still in evidence in Cemaes Bay, as Philip and Daniel drove along the *Ffordd y Traeth*, or Beach Road, toward Park Lodge on that mild Saturday afternoon a few days later. The tide had receded from the harbour and seagulls screeched as they swooped over the beach, searching for crabs or shellfish exposed on the damp sand.

Daniel and Jill bounced enthusiastically from the car when Philip pulled up alongside the sheep-handling pens on the farm; John Owen was already there and had filled the sheep dip with water. John's well-made sheep dip was one of many that he had constructed for farmers all over the Island. The thick, black, oily liquid that he was pouring into the sheep dip, curdled into a milky coffee brown as it swirled and blended with the water, while a chokingly pungent smell of disinfectant filled the air. Sally, the vet, was standing ready and prepared to treat the hooves of any limping sheep, while Steve hobbled over painfully on his crutches to greet his helpers, with a warm, appreciative smile.

"Sorry about the leg, Steve," Philip said sympathetically as Steve's wife Irene joined the group and thanked them for coming.

"I just did not expect it," Steve replied, shaking his head dolefully. "I knew he was a strong ram, but I was unprepared for him to be so mean-tempered!"

"So, what will you do with him?" Philip asked.

"Well, I can't keep him with his devilish temperament, not with footpaths crossing the land and campers spending their holidays here on the farm. I will keep him until he has done his work for this season and then I will sell him," Steve replied, with painful conviction as he gestured toward the pen where Rufus skittered around irritably, testing it for an escape route. "I would happily send him straight to the 'knacker', but he is far too valuable for that." Philip was suddenly reminded of the sad outcome for Caesar and tried to put it to the back of his mind.

"Be careful, Daniel, don't get too close!" Philip called out, as Daniel watched in fascination at the colours blending in the sheep dip. "And go upwind, so you don't breathe in the fumes, they are not good for you." Daniel backed off obediently and sat down on a hay bale next to Jill; he loved working with his Dad and so did Jill; however, the temptation to discipline the noisy, boisterous flock of sheep jostling with one another in the pens, meant Jill had to be tied up where she could not disrupt the proceedings.

The dipping went swiftly and smoothly, according to plan. As Steve's wife, Irene released the sheep from the pen, so Sally was kept busy trimming the hooves of any limping sheep before they entered the sheep-dip. Then Philip guided them, one by one down into the dip, where they swam frantically towards the far end. John then used a broom to duck their heads under the water before they clambered out.

After an hour or so, the last ewe galloped off after her ordeal, with an antelope-like leap into the lush green pasture. Straightening up, Philip and John took a few minutes to recover before tackling Rufus who was causing quite a commotion in his pen.

"He has developed a bit of a limp since he has been here," Steve announced, much to the consternation of everyone involved. Philip and John grimaced at each other, for it was evident that Rufus would not take kindly to being tossed onto his rear end to permit Sally to trim his hooves!

"This will be a two-man job, I can see, John," Philip said as they both strode toward the pen, which was being challenged to contain the 'big ugly beast'. Daniel watched from his seat next to Jill, affectionately rubbing her ears to calm her. She lurched forwards a few times in a vain effort to assist her master in controlling Rufus, who had made a determined lunge at the gate and looked set to break it down. Irene opened the gate gingerly, while Philip and John made a grab at the short wool of Rufus' back, intending to upend him.

"Oh, my back! My back!" John groaned suddenly and Philip watched in dismay as John limped away in agony toward a hay bale, sitting down hard and rubbing the offending injury. "Sorry, Philip," he moaned apologetically, "I can't do it; it's an old injury bothering me. Sorry." Philip could not answer; it took all of his strength and concentration to try to gain the mastery over Rufus, who was kicking and scuffing the concrete yard with his back legs and refusing to comply.

With a violent writhe and a twist, that titan managed to turn around to face Philip, planting its hooves firmly on his shoulders. Standing erect that way, Rufus was easily as tall as Philip's six-foot frame, so they met each other nose to nose; evil-looking amber eyes staring directly and threateningly into Philip's startled blue ones. With Rufus breathing hot and intimidatingly into Philip's face and Philip wishing his dancing partner had better-smelling breath, the two of them wrestled in a vigorous *Tango*. Neither of them was willing to cede as they struggled together, rocking backwards and forwards, around the courtyard.

The two ladies, who had attempted to intervene, thought better of it and retired to sit next to Steve, who was annoyed at himself for being just a helpless spectator. Jill, sensing that all was not going according to plan, started barking excitedly, while Daniel attempted to restrain her from involving herself in the battle.

John Owen, however, was in hysterics! He had given up rubbing his back and was now holding onto his sides with unbridled laughter as Philip and Rufus swung together, each trying to take the lead in their *Paso Doble!*

"John! Stop laughing!" Philip managed to call over his shoulder. John was too far-gone though; he was rocking on his hay bale seat with tears of mirth running down his face.

"Sorry, Philip; sorry," he replied, unsuccessfully trying to sound serious. "But you look as if you are dancing with the Devil!" Then he exploded with another fit of laughter.

The power struggle between man and ram continued for several more minutes, much to the entertainment of their audience, with Philip beginning to doubt he would have the strength or energy to gain the mastery of that obstinate animal. However, Jill, who knew exactly how to handle the errant brute, suddenly broke free from her restraining rope beside Daniel, and hurled herself at Rufus giving him a disciplinary, hard bite on one of his back legs. Rufus was caught off-guard by this unexpected assault, just long enough for Philip to gain the battle and swiftly toss the beast onto his rear end with all four feet off the ground, immobilising him, ready for Sally to carry out his pedicure.

Once that had been accomplished, John rallied, and it took the strength of both men to force Rufus into the sheep dip. He was so big that he had to be doused with several buckets of the chemical mix over his back, to make sure that he was thoroughly treated, while he kicked and bucked like a rodeo horse splashing in a child's paddling pool.

"'Dancing with the Devil' eh, John?" Philip looked sideways at John with a wry smile on his face as they sat on hay bales, enjoying a well-deserved beer with Steve after their exhausting experience. The two ladies chatted over a *panad* together, while Daniel, who was having an exciting day, was relishing his lemonade and ice-lollies.

"Sorry, Philip; sorry," John repeated, looking like he was threatening to burst into hysterics again. "But you did look funny together; with his ears sticking up like horns and that evil look on his face, he looked really devilish!" Thankfully, Philip saw the funny side of it, despite his aching back, and he began to chuckle.

"Yes, I must admit, there were moments when I thought the

same thing myself," he replied; "but Jill saved the day, didn't you, Jill?" He gave Jill a congratulatory pat on the back, and Jill's tail beat happily against the rough concrete floor, her warm amber eyes a total contrast to those of Rufus, glowing with adoration for her beloved master.

"Even if you are not supposed to bite the sheep, I must say I am glad you came along with us today!"

36 The Barbecue

"What a lovely day for a barbecue!" my sister Candy said with theatrical loudness after the Service that Sunday morning.

"Barbecue?" repeated Lorraine, the minister's wife, who had been chatting with a group of ladies nearby.

"Barbecue?" Several of the ladies repeated excitedly. "What a good idea!"

"I have a pound of sausages in my freezer," Lorraine volunteered.

"Yes, so do I, and I can bring some lemonade," Bridget added. Within seconds we had everyone's attention and offers of food, drink and contributions started coming thick and fast.

"But I just cleaned the kitchen carpet, Candy," I whispered between clenched teeth and a false smile.

"Don't worry; it will be warm enough for everyone to stay outside," Candy assured me.

"Well, we will have to see what Philip says," I replied, hoping he might be too busy that day. "But I won't be up to doing much to help," I continued, caressing my 'bump' to remind her that I was now five months pregnant and feeling rather delicate.

By early afternoon, the cars started to arrive; children poured out of them and raced past the kitchen door to join their friends on the fields at the back of our house where Philip was recruiting helpers to build a bonfire. Their fathers poked their heads in briefly to give a polite greeting before depositing contributions of beer and lemonade on the picnic table outside. Meanwhile, their mothers clambered over the baby gate I had erected at the kitchen door in the hope of keeping at least some visitors on the other side of it.

"Where is that awful smell coming from?" demanded Sharon as she handed me a box of beef burgers.

"Yes, it's terrible! What is causing it?" The other ladies asked, emboldened by Sharon's forthright question. Ah, yes, that had been another of my defence strategies to keep everyone out of the kitchen and hopefully protect my newly-cleaned carpet: the goose eggs in the incubator.

"Had you thought of raising geese?" John Owen had suggested; "I know someone who has fertilised eggs for sale and he may even loan you his incubator." Well, we had followed the instructions very carefully, spraying them with tepid water and turning those six eggs daily for the last few weeks. However, four of them had exploded in the incubator, leaving only two hopefuls and at least one of them was responsible for the foul smell!

Unfortunately, that did not deter the ladies from seeking the warmth and comfort of the kitchen and before long the room was packed, wall to wall with enthusiastic cooks and organisers. Most of us were refugees from stressful lives in English towns or cities, who found not only peace on Anglesey but also, sadly, unemployment and hard times.

"I could only find a bag of onions," Tracy apologised, as she passed her donation over the baby gate so that she could scale it herself. She was a beautiful lady, with long, fair hair, who had given up a career as a model in order to raise her family in the countryside.

"What can I do to help?" She offered exuberantly, and then wrinkled her pretty nose at the smell emanating from the corner of the room, although she was too polite to comment on it. Colin and Bridget did not stand on ceremony, however.

"Ugh! What is that awful smell?" They demanded loudly, as they dislodged the ineffective baby gate and marched into the kitchen. Bridget placed a hastily prepared, but delicious-looking Victoria Sandwich on the kitchen table, while her husband went straight over to the source of the offending odour.

"How long have you had them?" Colin asked in his strong Liverpool accent.

"Ooh, about a month," I responded, wondering what was coming next.

"They're dead!" he stated mercilessly. "You need to throw them out."

"Maybe later," I countered; "we want to give them a fair chance."

The delicious aroma of onions cooking on the Rayburn began to waft through the kitchen, slightly masking the stench of the eggs and temporarily distracting our visitors.

"So, what is happening with your barn?" Bridget asked, as Sharon set down a pot of tea on the table and added a collection of mugs she had found in the cupboard. Sharon knew our kitchen quite well, so I was grateful to be able to sit in the corner beside the smelly eggs, with Saffron on my lap and allow the ladies to take control of the catering.

"We are still waiting for council permission to finish building it," I replied unhappily.

"No! Really? What is the hold-up?" Tracy asked in surprise, as she added a spoonful of sugar to her cup of tea and several friends gathered around the table to hear my answer.

"Apparently, someone lodged a complaint that we were building a chapel up here, so the council sent a man to check it out and he put an instant ban on our building the barn 'until further notice'!" I was irritated, they could tell.

"How unkind!" was the consensus in the room, along with interjections such as: "Who would have done that?" and "Whatever made them think you needed to build a chapel?"

"We honestly do not know," I had to admit. "All the neighbours we have met have been very kind and helpful, but I really hope we will be allowed to finish the barn before the baby is born." We were still bewildered ourselves; we could not imagine who would have been so spiteful as to try to put a stop to the work and beyond our immediate neighbours, how could anyone have been able to make out the owl holes and mistake them for crosses? Perhaps the post man or the coal man had made an innocent comment about the appearance of the barn in the hearing of the offended neighbour. However, we were sure that, if they had done so, it would not have been mal-intended since both were jolly and well-meaning and we considered them as friends.

With the heat of the Rayburn warming the room, the smell of the goose eggs became overwhelming, causing the bevy of tea drinkers in the kitchen to thin and set up camp around the bonfire, leaving just a small team of tenacious 'troopers' to continue preparing the food. I was surprised to see Greg and Shirley's three boys scoot past the open back door toward the bonfire; I had not heard another car pull up in the driveway, so how did they get here I wondered and where were their parents? A few minutes later, their mother, Shirley arrived at the door, flushed and out of breath.

"I am in a bit of trouble!" she gasped, brushing back her heavy dark fringe from her perspiring face and clinging to the door frame for support.

"What is it, Shirley?" I asked, genuinely concerned. "Come in and have a cup of tea." I took her by the arm and sat her down at the table.

"I took a wrong turning," Shirley said between sips of tea; "I left the car down there because I was afraid of going down the ditch."

"Ah, that would explain why I didn't hear your car pull up," I commented. "Didn't Greg come with you?"

"No, he is not well today," Shirley took another sip of tea and reached for one of the biscuits I offered. "But my word, what a long driveway you have; I don't know how you manage to walk up and down there several times a day!" She leaned back on her chair and took a few more deep breaths. "Do you think you could ask Philip to come and tow me please? I am quite worried about leaving the car on your neighbour's driveway."

"I will ask him," I assured her and at that moment Amelia appeared at the back door in search of a drink of water, so I took advantage of the opportunity. "Amelia, Love, would you run and ask Daddy if he would help 'Aunty' Shirley with her car please?" Amelia returned a few minutes later with the message that Philip was busy organising some games just then, but he would come as soon as he could. Time ticked by as Sharon and Candy continued to work over the Rayburn, dutifully cooking and preparing the food that had been contributed. I went out into the garden a few times to peer over the wall leading to the field and sure enough, Philip was still organising the games for the youngsters. Some members of the group were practising barn-dancing routines, while the men were stoking up the fire and distributing the drinks. Meanwhile, despite a few more cups of tea and biscuits, Shirley was becoming increasingly distraught.

"I think your neighbours will be very angry with me for blocking their driveway," she repeated frequently.

"Come on, I know how to tow; let's go!" I announced decisively. "Candy, would you please keep an eye on Saffron for me?"

All my practice at tow-starting the tractor was going to come in handy today, I thought to myself, as I eyed that red monster, still perched tauntingly on the top fields. I slid into the driver's seat of the Volvo beside Shirley, while my loyal little friend, Amelia, climbed into the back. I was not familiar with the track that Shirley asked me to take, but I knew there were a few houses down there.

"Just here!" Shirley declared and as I turned abruptly into the driveway she pointed to, there was her car, balancing precariously and threatening to drop down into the ditch.

"Ooh! I see what you mean," I said, stopping the car within a few feet of the abandoned vehicle. "Are you sure you couldn't drive it out yourself Shirley?"

"No, I could not!" Shirley replied emphatically. "I would definitely go down that ditch if I tried! Couldn't you drive it out?"

"I wouldn't like to take a chance," I was adamant about that, "not with my being five months pregnant." We sat in the car and thought about the problem for a while, despite being conscious that the owners of the house could arrive at any moment.

"OK, let's give it a go!" I said eventually. "You managed to get out of the car all right Shirley, so if you slide in from the passenger seat, you should be able to get back into the driver's seat safely. Give me a wave when you are ready and I will tow you out." Shirley agreed reluctantly but she did as instructed while I turned my car around and attached the towrope to both vehicles.

"Are you ready?" I called from my open window and in the rear-view mirror I could see Shirley give me the wave. As I inched forwards and Shirley's car lurched into motion, I began to hope that we were winning. Unfortunately, Shirley had omitted to turn

on the ignition, so the steering lock came on and, instead of the clean sweep to safety that I had hoped for, Shirley's worst fear became a reality and her car dropped down into the ditch!

"I think you had better run back and tell Daddy what has happened please, Amelia," I suggested as she and I surveyed that dreadful scene. Amelia ran off obediently on her 'important mission'; her long blond ponytail swishing from side to side as I watched her disappear around the bend.

Shirley and I stood on the driveway together, glancing at each other with unspoken mutual accusation. It had not been easy for her to struggle out of the passenger door of her car with it being positioned at such an awkward angle and she was somewhat irritable when she eventually managed to do so.

"Ah! Here comes the neighbour." I said, pleased to have a bit of distraction. Shirley did not seem to share my optimism, as the woman, who I had never seen before, came striding purposefully down her driveway towards us.

"Oh, dear," Shirley stammered nervously, "she does not look very pleased to see us!"

"No, don't worry," I reassured her. "She will be all right; she is my neighbour after all, maybe she will offer us a cup of tea while we wait for help to arrive." My positive spirit began to wither however, as the woman drew nearer. She was a rather large lady, with a tight perm in her short, dark hair and a threatening look on her face. Stomping ominously closer, she stood stock still at about twenty feet distance from us, her legs astride the driveway as she assumed a 'power stance', much like a French policeman. Folding her arms across her voluminous bosom, she glared at us and I suddenly knew what it must feel like to be a fly caught in a spider's web!

"There are two tracks here," the woman said with a strong Manchester accent, after several seconds of intimidating silence. "One for your right wheel and one for your left," she continued, unfolding her arms to demonstrate. "So, what are you doing in my ditch?"

Shirley plucked at my sleeve, evidently hopeful that I would be the spokesperson.

"I am very sorry about this, but my husband will be here soon to get us out," I assured the woman.

"You are 'that lot' up there, aren't you?" she spat insultingly, pointing toward *Tŷ'n Llain* and all thought of 'a nice cup of tea together', rapidly disappeared. "Well, we don't want you here; you with that chapel you are building up there!"

I stared open-mouthed at her as sudden realisation dawned on me. 'It was you!' I said to myself. 'It was you who sent the building inspector up to us! But how did you know about the barn? You cannot see our house from here; you must have snuck up there while we were out. You nasty lady!' I was so fuming that I said nothing and just turned my back on her.

"Well, you had better get that vehicle off my land soon," she launched at us. "My husband will be back any minute and he will need to get past." I was too angry and affronted to answer her and after a few seconds, we heard the thud of her solid shoes on the ground as she marched her way heavily back to her house.

We were relieved to see Philip on his tractor coming to our rescue a short while later, flanked by a small army of our friends from the barbecue. It crossed my mind to wonder who had been enlisted to tow-start the tractor this time, or did it manage to roll down the hill and start itself? Regardless, I was so pleased to see it this time and even quite proud of the way that, under Philip's skilful management, it so capably pulled Shirley's car out from its predicament. I suddenly felt an uncustomary warm glow of affection for our little red 'Fergie'.

The welcome aroma of lightly charred meat filled the air, as we returned from our disastrous experience. The tractor chugged its way triumphantly back up the lane to its exalted position on the top fields, while Shirley's poor car limped behind it and stationed itself on the front driveway. There was damage for sure that would need some attention at a local garage, but not today. The members of the rescue team, who had chatted happily together on their walk back to the house, made a beeline for the drinks table, where the sound of beer cans cracking open added to the festivity. Shirley and I sat in the kitchen, gratefully drinking the cup of tea that we had missed out on at the neighbour's place and Shirley even succumbed to a large glass of sherry to calm her nerves.

"Well, I am glad we were able to escape before the husband arrived," Shirley giggled, as the sherry began to take effect. "If he was anything like his wife..." She did not need to finish her sentence; I knew exactly what she meant. Yes, I had something to tell Philip later about my discovery.

"That smell is terrible!" Colin stated emphatically, as he came back into the kitchen to see if Bridget had finished cooking the next batch of sausages. It was true; the smell from the incubator was doing an excellent job of keeping most of our guests outside, but it was certainly getting worse.

"Look; I will do you a favour," he said and he strode across the kitchen and opened the lid of the incubator. The smell was incredible and a cluster of little girls who had gathered at the back door to ask to use the toilet, thought better of it, deciding they could wait. Lifting out the two remaining goose eggs from the incubator, Colin marched out of the back door, with me following rapidly behind him in protestation. Hurrying toward the concrete stile, he hurled the eggs to the ground on the other side of it under a hawthorn tree. There, the 'Mother of all stink-bombs' burst open, spewing out ghastly green and revoltingly putrid slime!

"Oh!" I said, holding my nose and peering over the wall at the horrible mess on the ground.

"Yes; 'Oh'!" Colin repeated triumphantly as an assortment of children gathered around to see what was going on. He did not need to say, 'I told you so!'

The children started falling around with their hands covering their noses, making nauseated noises of revulsion, and calling to their friends to come to join in the fiasco. I did not know what bothered me most, the fact that we had lovingly nurtured unfertilised eggs for the last few weeks, or the problem of knowing how to get rid of those two toxic puddles. However, Colin grabbed a spade, gathered a mound of soil from some molehills, threw it over the offensive, stinking pools and the smell disappeared instantly.

"So that's that then," I ceded, still standing beside the concrete stile and caressing my baby, Oliver, to soothe him as he kicked inside me in response to my anxiety. I was understandably disappointed, but I guessed that I had known the truth about the eggs for some time now.

With that matter quite firmly resolved, and the identity of the accusing neighbour discovered, my only remaining concern was that, with evening coming on and the fumes no longer emitting from the incubator, the kitchen would suffer increased invasion, meaning the carpet would need scrubbing again tomorrow. But tomorrow was another day. I watched as Colin and Bridget disappeared through the field gate with the next batch of cooked sausages, and I decided it was time to take my cup of tea and join the joyful assembly in the field. All the children were laughing and running around happily; the music started up and almost everyone joined in the barn dancing beside the bonfire, which was sending sparks and spits wafting prettily up into the still evening air. It was a remarkably successful barbecue.

37 Turning Back the Clock

As Philip sat waiting in the room, he had time to reflect on the reason for his being there and the strange circumstances that had led to it...

All eyes were upon the tall, slender beauty as she glided gracefully into the room and took her place at her desk. Philip thought she was the prettiest lady he had ever seen, and his big blue eyes grew wide with amazement as they watched her. He wondered what he could do to let her know of his admiration and decided to write her a letter. However, his stubby little five-year-old fingers just could not work that pencil to form the words he wanted to say to please her. Ten years later, he still struggled to read or write despite the best efforts of Miss Clarke, his kindly and attractive first teacher, and every other teacher since that first day at Crofton Ann Dale County Primary School.

"You turn fifteen today, Barlow," the headmaster of Bishopfield Secondary School stated when he called him into his office. Philip had fidgeted uncomfortably on the brown leather office chair, scuffing his feet noisily over the polished parquet flooring.

"Yes, Sir," replied that unkempt young man, keeping his eyes on the floor and smiling nervously. Visits to the *deputy* headmaster's office had never been an enjoyable experience, but this was the first time he had been sent to the office of the school headmaster himself.

"That means you can leave now," the headmaster specified as he fixed him with an eye full of meaning and a disconcertingly false smile. Philip found eye contact difficult at the best of times but, in this situation, it was virtually impossible. He struggled to understand the significance of the statement; the headmaster was not brandishing a cane, with which he was used to being punished on his visits to the deputy headmaster's office.

His class teacher who had regularly sent him for trips to that disagreeable room had been surprisingly pleasant to him recently. It must have been about two weeks since he had been called to the front of the class and made to bend over for his weekly beating with a slipper for being the class Dunce. Even the P.E. teacher had not humiliated him recently for his inability to catch that ball. Philip's eyes had explored the unfamiliar room for clues as to why he was there at that moment; anything but making eye contact with the man on the other side of the desk. A clock ticked quietly on the wall, and the headmaster started tapping his pencil to its rhythm on his pristine, polished desk. To Philip, it was like the sinister drum beat accompanying someone walking to his execution. He began to tweak nervously at the lapel of his ill-fitting blazer.

School life had never been a joy for Philip by any stretch of the imagination and his years at Bishopfield Secondary School had been particularly difficult. He had often wondered why he could not have been like so many other boys in the school, who were such great achievers academically. He had suffered terribly from teasing and bullying by the other students because of being 'different', a circumstance exacerbated by being repeatedly humiliated by some of his teachers.

"That means you can leave ...now!" the headmaster slowly

repeated with emphasis. Philip scratched meditatively at the downy hair beginning to form on his upper lip and rubbed at his knee, a habit he had developed when he felt nervous. He needed a moment or two to compute this new situation.

"Now, Sir?" he choked out feebly, making brief and uncomfortable eye contact with his nemesis. From the intense look on the headmaster's face, Philip gathered this was a serious statement. "You mean right away, now, Sir?" he asked again to be sure he had the right message. The headmaster smiled and nodded without releasing his victim from his unyielding and pervasive stare.

"Goodbye, Barlow; I wish you all the best," he said insincerely. Philip rose from his seat, scuffed his way to the door and, remembering his manners, turned as he opened it.

"Thank you, Sir," he replied. "Goodbye, Sir." With his hands folded on his shiny wooden desktop, the headmaster continued his broad, fake smile as Philip passed through the doorway and closed it carefully behind him. As he walked alone up the path leading out of the school premises that day, he pondered over the fact that this was his very last day at school, even though there was yet another month left before the end of the term when he was expecting to leave. Much as he disliked school, Philip had spent many quiet evenings imagining the school-leaving party, the 'whoop' of delight and the celebrations he might have shared with the rest of the class. Standing outside on the pavement, he turned and looked back at the school where he had spent the last four years of his young life. There was no fanfare, no fond farewells, no recommendations to any future employer and no idea what to do next. He knew he was not stupid, but he wondered if he would ever understand the reason for his inability to put thoughts onto paper. If only there had then been a better understanding of *dyslexia* and what an accomplished man he would become.

As he sat waiting for his new teacher almost twenty years later, Philip considered how bizarre it was that he should be here voluntarily, given his past experiences with the education system.

The interview had gone reasonably well with the efficient young man representing the Welsh Development Agency, or W.D.A.

"This is a highly irregular request, Mr Barlow," Martin Davis had said, his eyebrows disappearing into the fringe of his fire-red curls. "The positions available at Coleg Pencraig are reserved for people who have been on the unemployment list for at least a year."

"I understand that," Philip had replied respectfully. "But let's face it, you and I both know there is very little likelihood of my finding work here, and I will be hopelessly unemployed from now on. So why not save the taxpayer's money and give me this position right now?" Martin Davis had leaned his elbows on the desk in front of him and rested his chin on his clasped hands as he looked across at the objective man who was only a few years older than himself. He considered him a refreshing contrast to some of the other applicants enrolling on the scheme. He tapped his pencil on the desk while he thought about the situation, reminding Philip of that last uncomfortable interview with the headmaster of Bishopfield Secondary School.

"It will be a one-year course, which W.D.A will pay for, along with any related fees," Martin Davis' statement had brought Philip's attention back to the present. "You will also receive an allowance to help with your living costs, but it will be set at the rate of 90% of what you would have received if you were on unemployment benefit."

"That's OK; we can manage," Philip had assured him, elated that his persistence was paying off.

So, here he was on the brink of starting the new school year at Coleg Pencraig, Llangefni, on a course specializing in Horticulture, and he was determined to make a success of it.

The clock ticked quietly on the wall as he waited nervously to meet the head of the Horticulture Department. Would the man he was waiting for be kind to him, Philip wondered, or would he be austere and unpleasant? At nine am precisely, the door burst open and a man, possibly in his mid-forties, burst into the room. He was of medium height, slim, with a thick thatch of unruly dark brown hair and a neatly trimmed beard.

"Ah! Mr Barlow?" the man asked, with a genuine smile as he reached across and shook Philip's hand vigorously. "Alan Savage," he announced, sounding a little out of breath as though he had just run the last few miles to the college. "I hope you have not been waiting too long?" Alan Savage was dressed casually in an open-necked blue checked shirt tucked into his buff-coloured twill trousers. Swinging his black leather shoulder bag onto a nearby shelf, he slumped unceremoniously into his office chair at the desk opposite where Philip sat, open-mouthed with surprise at the unpretentious presentation of the man who was to be his mentor for the coming year.

"So, you are interested in doing the horticultural course...um...Philip?" he queried, after searching amongst the disorderly mound of papers, books, folders and coffee cups on his desk for Philip's C.V. "Hmmm...you have had quite a bit of experience in Horticulture according to this, but no previous qualifications I see." Philip had worked very hard to improve his handwriting, so he was relieved that Alan Savage found the information legible.

"Hmmm...I see," said Alan Savage, nodding his head and looking up to meet Philip's anxious gaze. "You worked in a nursery when you first left school?" he continued.

"Yes, I did," Philip replied. "I learned several skills in the propagation of fruit and ornamental trees and shrubs while I was there."

"But you did not receive any qualifications?" Alan Savage looked surprised.

"Sadly, no," Philip admitted. "I was promised day release to Sparsholt College, Winchester, but that did not happen. But I am pleased to have the opportunity to gain the City and Guilds Certificate this time."

"So, you have worked in commercial apple tree pruning, been team manager in strawberry fields, and owned a landscaping business in Kent and Hampshire," Alan Savage continued, returning his attention to the paperwork in front of him. "Have you had any experience in cut flowers?"

"No, Sir, but I am willing to learn," Philip assured him.

"Well, Philip; call me Alan," he invited, rubbing his forefinger across his moustache as he thought for a moment. "I believe Phase One will be too easy for you, so I suggest that, if we can persuade the W.D.A. to finance you, you could do Phase Two alongside Phase One. What do you think?" Philip's eyes lit up at this suggestion, and he readily agreed. Perhaps here was his chance to turn back the clock and have another opportunity to be a successful student.

"Then, let's get going!" Alan said decisively, as he stood up, gathered the pages of Philip's CV, stapled them together and tossed them back onto his desk along with the rest of the debris strewn there. "Phase One starts today and every Monday; Phase Two is every Tuesday, and then you will work with Commercial Floristry for the rest of the week." Picking up his bag and swinging it over his shoulder, Alan Savage opened the office door and ushered Philip through it to start on his exciting new venture.

38 Handfuls of Toads

"One squashed toad, two squashed toads," the children were making revolting, squelchy 'squashed toad' noises and imitations of the poor contorted corpses that lined the lane in the wake of Philip's departure earlier that morning. Jill skipped happily ahead of us, her white-tipped tail swishing from side to side with the excitement of escorting her children to the school bus.

"Ten squashed toads, eleven squashed toads..."

"OK, everyone, I think that's enough!" I interrupted. Although the toad population at *Tŷ'n Llain* was prolific, especially with it being so damp at that time of year, Philip and I were saddened at the loss of life and wondered how we could avoid causing it. There were toads everywhere; toads hopped around the garden, hid in our boots outside the back door, and the children gathered handfuls of them from the water troughs in the paddocks.

Nonetheless, it was one of those refreshing mornings when it felt good to be alive and one of those rare mornings when I managed to be on time for the school bus. Elaine, the bus driver, had an agreeable disposition and a tousle of curly ginger hair atop her cheerful, freckled face. She enjoyed her daily mission to collect and deliver her 'Mountain children' to and from the little school in Llanfechell, and she seemed pleasantly surprised to see us all sitting waiting for her on the low stone wall at the end of the lane when she arrived. It would be my new resolution to be on time from now on, I told her, and she gave me a cheeky smile that told me she did not have the same confidence in my conviction.

Daniel had started attending *Ysgol* Sir Thomas Jones, the Secondary School in Amlwch, with the new school year and would catch the coach to school from the bottom of the lane at about eight am. Our children had been disappointed to leave their school in Cemaes Bay; however, since Philip had returned PJ's motorbike and started at Coleg Pencraig in Llangefni, it had been necessary for them to change to a more local school. We had no worries about the standard of education our children would receive at Llanfechell School since we knew the education systems of North Wales are focused on ensuring their schools provide a level of teaching that is second to none. What concerned us was the matter of language, nationalism and integration for our children. Cymraeg, or Welsh, is understandably the first language in this region, and it would be naïve to expect otherwise. Welsh, as spoken by the indigenous people, is indeed the language of the bards (poets); it seems to make men sound more masculine, women more feminine, and is so melodious when used in song.

It would be a grave mistake to think of Wales as just another part of England, for although willingly subject to the sovereignty of British Royalty and government, Wales is a distinctly separate country and culture. Being of almost pure Celtic origin, it is no wonder Welsh people have such a strong feeling of national identity. The big question for us was how well our children would fit into this school and how well would they be accepted and treated. Time would tell.

My musings kept me occupied during my walk back up the lane; it was not the most comfortable of rides for Saffron in her pushchair as the recent heavy rainfall had washed away some more of the lane's surface. Jill zigzagged behind us impatiently to speed our progress since she knew there was much work to be done on the farm. We passed Diesel, the Shetland pony, grazing in his paddock at *Bryn Egor,* and at the sight of passers-by, Arthur's dog, Gel, at *Pencae,* ran excitedly up and down on her lead, which was attached to a pulley wheel on a cable running the length of the property.

I felt healthy with this pregnancy and light of step as I walked purposefully back home. Autumn was already in evidence, and although it was only mid-September, the leaves on the Goat willows were already starting to drop, and the dew-covered blackberry bushes were a stunning mixture of colours ranging from emerald to scarlet and purple. Nothing too much was expected of September; it came between the hope of having at least a show of summer and the inevitable frightening winds of October.

Rounding the bend at the top of the lane and taking the fork for *Tŷ'n Llain*, I suddenly stopped and stared in astonishment! The sun was just tipping the top of the mountain with a golden halo, sending piercing beams of light filtering through the quivering dew drops on an expansive cobweb strung across the branches of a low willow. A globular orb spider sat in its centre, proudly displaying her boldly-patterned back, like a shield bearing a coat of arms. Saffron and I watched in wonderment as the sun rose, causing an explosion of the colours of the spectrum that sparkled red, orange, yellow, green, blue, indigo and violet through those shimmering watery prisms. That exquisite vision kept us transfixed for several minutes while the sun rose further and bathed the mountain with its warm light.

Saffron was fascinated by the scene; she always enjoyed watching the activities of insects and other small creatures, and since being mobile, she would rummage in the flower border for snails. Unfortunately for them, she loved the squishy feel when she poked her finger into their crisp shells, no matter how often I forbade her to do so. One day, however, she noticed a snail trekking purposefully across the pathway with its intricately patterned shell perched on its back and its little antennae waving while leaving a silvery trail of slime behind it.

"Daddy," she asked, with her big blue eyes full of surprise as she pointed at this strange discovery "Is that ...?"

"Yes, Saffron," Philip answered; "that is a snail." We could tell from the expression on her face that it had suddenly dawned on her just what damage she had been doing and she never did it again.

Saffron

"This is how I carry boys!" I told my midwife, Sue Eagan, when she came for her weekly visit later that day; I was confident of my diagnosis as I had also carried both of our boys healthily and with no problems.

"We shall wait and see," Sue Eagan replied sagely. In those days, they did not do regular scans unless the midwife had concerns over the position or health of the baby, so the parents were usually just prepared for a surprise on its arrival. Well, there was so much to do around the farm that it was just as well I was healthy. With Philip being at college and the money he had earned from working at Rhosgoch needing to be carefully rationed for us to survive the coming year on a low income, I was kept extremely busy. I had planted a selection of winter vegetables in the vegetable garden that Philip had dug over, and virtually every morsel of food we ate was home-made, healthful and nutritious. But that was how it was for most of our friends there on Anglesey, however, where employment was scarce and money was short.

We delighted in sourcing free food from the fields and hedgerows, such as nettles and mushrooms for soup and meadowsweet blossoms to make champagne. Meadowsweet champagne, brewed over the summer months, was a tasty social mixer. It was extremely lively after a week when we bottled it, while after three weeks, it was positively explosive, and there were several stains on the kitchen ceiling to prove it. It was amusing to watch our visitors experience the effervescent consequences of opening one of those pressurised bottles when we handed it to them at mealtime.

Our relatives and friends from 'The South' must have considered us the poorest of the poor, for whenever they came to visit, they would bring donations of large, black plastic sacks of second-hand clothes for us to distribute among ourselves. From those sacks I had amassed quite a collection of beautiful baby boy's clothes for our little Oliver, who was due in December. Our children thought they were so fortunate to have such a selection of lovely outfits, and they had not the least idea that we were living on such a tight budget.

Watch me, Dad! Watch me!" Joshua was excited to take his first turn on the 'Flying Fox' aerial slide Philip had made. About a year earlier, he had built a small wooden tree house for the children in the sycamore trees lining the lane, and it was from there he had now run the aerial slide, which finished against a cushioned post in the lower fields. They all loved it! Philip and I stood together near the Flying Fox terminus, offering encouraging comments to our young ones as they shot past us, one after the other, in a seemingly endless procession.

'This field would make a wonderful cricket pitch,' I thought as I looked out across the lower fields on that mild Saturday afternoon, and I was just about to say so when Philip 'pipped me to the post'.

"This field would make a wonderful strawberry patch," he said, scanning the terrain with a distant look in his eyes.

"Oh, I was just thinking what a good playground it would make for the children," I countered. "It is the flattest one we have."

"The college is going to plough over their strawberry patch, so if you like, I could dig up all the runners and bring them home for us to plant." It sounded as though he had been thinking this over for a while.

"There is enough room here for a good-sized cricket pitch," I added.

"It has good drainage, with deep acidic soil and is in a sunny position, all ideal for strawberries," Philip continued, as though he had not heard a word I had said.

"Maybe a section could be reserved for swings and a seesaw," I persisted. My townie upbringing was trying to have some impact on this country life I was leading.

"With just half an acre, we could produce one and a half tons of strawberries, which should sell for about fifteen hundred pounds. As we will be doing all the planting ourselves, there will be very little expense involved," Philip was on a roll, so there was no point in trying to interrupt the development of his calculated plans. I turned from contemplating my hopeful playground and looked at him directly; he was surveying the fields with the satisfied countenance of a Roman Centurion inspecting his troops. In his eyes, I could already see the reflection of ripe, red summer berries nestled amongst their golden straw beds, and I was getting the impression I was not going to win here.

The man with the tractor and plough arrived the following week; Philip had decided to get someone in to do the job as his attempts at ploughing straight lines had embarrassed him. The aroma of sweet humus filled the air, and the rich soil raised to the surface resembled the darkest of crumbling chocolate as the plough cut through the pasture and turned it over. It was evidently full of worms since a flurry of noisy seagulls followed the tractor, carrying off abundant booty.

It was a family affair, planting all those strawberry plants; Cambridge Favourite, Gorella and Hapil varieties, with everyone having their assignments according to their capabilities. I was only a month off from having our baby, so I did what I could to help; anything that did not involve too much bending. It took the whole weekend to complete the task, and the prospect of oodles of strawberries to eat the following summer, with lots of strawberry jam to see us through the winter, made it all seem worthwhile.

"How would you like it if we plant the rest of the field with flowers for drying next year?" Philip suggested as we sat on our

311

favourite rock to watch the sun setting gloriously behind Mynydd Y Garn. "I could plant the seeds, grow the seedlings on as plugs at college, and then we can transplant them to our field there. You could dry the flowers and sell them to the local florists or even make floral arrangements for sale."

"Lovely, Philip," I replied resignedly and without enthusiasm, although I had to admire his enterprising spirit.

"And how about we make a playground for the children just here, next to Jeffrey's field?" he added. And I thought he had not been listening.

39 Pleasant Surprises

"Do you have the goods?" Philip knew he would not be welcome unless he produced them. He raised one eyebrow and smiled a wry smile of conspiracy, then reaching inside his coat pocket, he pulled out the precious package.

"Only twelve?" I exclaimed. "That means just one every two hours until this time tomorrow!" Despite my misgivings, I popped one into my mouth and was in instant ecstasy. Eucalyptus sweets, I absolutely craved them! The price having been paid for entry, Philip hastened over the threshold and into the kitchen; he was starving.

Philip enjoyed being at the college; Alan savage was an excellent teacher who liked to share his knowledge of Horticulture and with his insatiable thirst for information, Philip soaked up each lesson. During the first week of the term, he had been pleasantly surprised to meet Blanche, our relief post lady. She was happy to report that Poppy was doing well and had produced two beautiful litters of puppies.

'Poppy, a lovely dog', tugged at my heartstrings every time I passed the fridge, where sad little messages and drawings of Poppy decorated the fridge door, alongside pictures of ballerinas and brown apples, increasing my sense of guilt at letting her go. However, Blanche's offer to take care of our mischievous little Jack Russell was indeed a relief.

"It was a happy day when Poppy came to live with us," Blanche beamed as they chatted in the potting shed together. "Because she is a tricolour, her puppies are quite valuable."

"Excellent!" Philip replied, pleased to see Blanche in good spirits again. "I hope she is behaving herself?"

"Of course," Blanche laughed. "She knows she is well-loved too." Philip was sure of that.

"So, what brings you here, Blanche?" he asked.

"The same as you, I suppose," Blanche answered, returning her attention contentedly to the chrysanthemum cuttings the team of workers were assigned to plant in the pots of compost. "I could not find employment after the Post Office job finished, then I saw this advertisement in the newspaper for the City and Guilds course in Floristry; I rather fancy myself as a florist."

"Siarad Cymraeg!" One of the Practical Horticultural instructors commanded, breaking rudely into their conversation. He had been conversing in the Welsh language on the other side of the table with Graham Thomas, who oversaw floristry. Philip and Blanche looked up from their happy employment, shocked at that sudden interruption commanding them to speak Welsh. It was not so much what he said that surprised Philip and Blanche as the vehemence with which it was delivered, indicating deep-seated nationalism behind it.

"Sorry, Wil," Philip replied after recovering his composure. "We will get there, but we are only just learning Welsh, so please give us a bit of time."

"Just joking, Philip," Wil Jones' face broke into a forced smile. Philip was not so sure about that; he had heard Wil ranting in the tea room about all these English coming into Wales and applying for jobs that should only be reserved for the Welsh. It struck Philip that, while at college, he would need to keep his head down and not cause any ripples, and he resolved to do just that. He worked diligently at any assignment, such as digging over the ground of the greenhouses and clearing sections of stony land ready for cultivation.

The course proved very beneficial to the family and not just for what Philip was learning. Every week, for the first three weeks, he came home from college bearing sacks full of beetroots. We made beetroot salad, beetroot soup, and beetroot borscht, we pickled

314

it, stewed it, grated it, made beetroot wine, and chocolate beetroot cakes, and we shared them with our friends and family. He also brought home stunning flowers such as chrysanthemums of various colours, either single stem or multi-headed, and gypsy, a delicate, miniature form of carnation, ranging from light to dark shades of pink. Alstroemeria in striking pink, orange or red, and lilies, which were large and white or petite with intense primary colours; all of them were rejects and unsaleable but still delightfully decorative.

The W.D.A. approved Philip's application to do Phases One and Two together; however, within two weeks he was invited into the office of Bryner Jones, the Head of Agriculture, who had a proposition to make. Bryner Jones was a very well-presented man, not tall but thickset with well-groomed black hair, and always dressed in a crisp shirt, tie and a tweed jacket.

"How are you getting on here, Philip?" he asked in a deep Welsh tone.

"I am delighted to be here, Mr Jones, thank you," Philip could say that honestly to the man, although he wondered why he had been invited to attend this interview.

"Mr Savage tells me you are doing very well and are managing your course admirably," Bryner Jones continued. Philip was pleased to hear that from the head of the department, considering this was the first time in his life he had received such commendation from a teacher.

"I am teaching two courses: Phase Three Agricultural Accounts and Agricultural Management," Mr Jones elaborated on his reason for calling this meeting. "And I believe from what I have heard that you could complete these courses when adapted for Horticulture."

"Well, thank you for your confidence, Mr Jones," Philip was pleasantly surprised and flattered by the suggestion. "If you think

I could do it, I would certainly be interested, but I cannot afford to pay for the course," he replied after a moment's consideration.

"No, I understand that," Mr Jones responded encouragingly. "We can apply to the W.D.A. to fund you; you only have a short while with us, so I think we should make the most of it. I must warn you that I will be teaching my courses in the Welsh language. But don't worry," he added quickly, seeing the apprehension on Philip's face. "I will ensure you understand what I am teaching during the lessons, and the examinations will be in English. Plus, we will book you in to do a course of half a day a week, learning spoken Welsh."

Philip's week began filling up fast and busily, with Horticultural studies on a Monday and Tuesday, Agricultural accounts on Thursday mornings, Agricultural management on Thursday afternoons, Welsh language on Friday mornings and cut flower production on Wednesday and Friday afternoons. Overall, being at Coleg Pencraig was a thoroughly enjoyable experience; the courses were well-taught in a relaxed and friendly environment, and all paid for by the Welsh Development Agency.

Philip was in his element. During the end-of-term holiday periods, he assisted in repairing dry stone walling in council-owned parkland and learned many skills necessary for looking after city parks and gardens. He was also involved in the eradication of an invasive species of rhododendron across Snowdonia, which was suppressing the native plants.

One Saturday afternoon two young men arrived at our house; they were brothers who wanted to start as sheep farmers and heard from John Owen that we had some excellent pedigree Suffolk ewes for sale. They were suitably impressed with Caesar's ewes as their health had improved remarkably over the months we had been caring for them. When Philip confirmed that most of them were expecting twins, the brothers were more than happy to pay the asking price of eighty pounds per ewe.

"What about that one; is she for sale too?" one of the young men asked when he caught sight of Dora, who appeared on the scene to see what was going on.

"Dora is more a family pet than a sheep, and she is only part-Suffolk," Philip replied honestly.

"Well, she looks in good shape; could we offer you eighty pounds for her as well?" the young men suggested after a brief consultation. Philip and I exchanged questioning glances, and I gave him a nod of approval; we needed the money, and apart from that, our children complained daily about her bullying. They were learning to be 'Dora smart', staying in a group when enlisted to take the vegetable peelings down to the chickens, since Dora, the farm 'highwayman', would leap out from her hiding place and accost them to steal the food. Despite that, we were sad to see her go, as she was one of our first lambs. However, the young farmers were delighted with their purchases, and we were sure they would care for her very well.

Gus and Nero were doing their duty admirably with the ewes in the paddocks, and we could have used the new barn for lambing in the spring if we were allowed to complete it. It was becoming an increasing source of irritation that the work on the new barn had been blocked for a whole year. Philip had stocked up the old barn with hay bales in readiness for the approaching winter, but it was so tiny, and he also needed to store his tools there.

I hoped we would have had permission to finish the work on the new barn before our baby was born, as I did not want Philip to be distracted at a time when I would need help around the house.

"A girl!" Candy's shocked voice could be heard from the telephone box all the way down the street, according to Christine, our builder's wife, who waited for her in the car. Candy was telephoning us after dropping our children at their school buses and then taking Saffron to my parents before collecting Christine to go to work. My dear sister had been an invaluable help, as always, having stayed at our house overnight while Philip and our midwife, Sue Eagan, spent the long hours in the hospital, aiding me give birth to our little one.

Yes, our midwife had been right to doubt my verdict; how healthily I carried our baby was no indicator of what sex it would be. So, Amelia now had not just one little sister but two! And what a little cutie was our Amber, with her pretty, petite face and full, rosebud lips she suited the name as though it had been reserved especially for her.

On the very day we returned home from *Ysbyty Gwynedd* with our beautiful baby on that chilly morning in mid-December, Dewi, the *postmon*, arrived at our house. He was delighted to hear of her safe arrival and cheerfully offered us his congratulations before handing Philip an official-looking brown envelope.

'Dear Mr Barlow,' the letter read. 'Having considered your situation, Llangefni County Council has the pleasure of informing you that you may now proceed with completing the building of your barn.'

"Mum! Mum! Come and look at this; I don't know what it is!" Daniel noticed it when he went outside to shake the tablecloth after dinner on that cold night a couple of weeks later. It was a strange sight, like a scarlet veil against the dark sky that stretched over Cemaes Bay and danced alluringly above the horizon. Although intriguing, it was also somewhat worrying since it hovered ominously over Wylfa power station.

"We will ask Dad when he gets in from working on the barn," I suggested after Daniel and I had stood transfixed for a while, watching that captivating phenomenon. "Come on inside now; it is getting too cold out here."

"Do you think it could be something to do with the power station, Mum?" Daniel was echoing my thoughts as we continued cleaning up the kitchen together.

"Maybe it is the streetlights of Cemaes reflecting on the sky, Daniel," I suggested, trying to distract him from his own imagination since he tended to be a worrier by nature. "Or perhaps people are practising with some fireworks ready for the New Year celebrations."

"Do you want me to empty the compost bucket, Mum?" Our other children were already sound asleep upstairs, but Daniel seemed happy to stay downstairs with me, proving to be particularly helpful that evening. I noticed he had found various reasons to slide outside several more times to see if there was any progress in that night sky display before going off to bed himself.

When Philip came in from the barn about an hour later, the veil of red light had become a shimmering curtain of ruby and emerald organza, which filled the northern sky and wafted exquisitely, as if blown by a gentle breeze. A large spot of crimson radiance had formed directly above the house, and from that central point, fine beams of deep red issued and curved down towards the north of us, so we felt as though we were looking up at the underside of a gigantic celestial dome.

"It has to be the Northern Lights," Philip confirmed my suspicions. "I have never seen anything like it." That spectacular performance lasted for quite some time, and we became almost oblivious to the biting cold as we stood together, mesmerized by the incredible, unforgettable experience. Life was good; Philip's college course was going well, and the prospects of finding work using the resulting qualifications looked hopeful. We had five adorable children, a warm and comfortable home, good friends and neighbours and a loving extended family. What the future held remained to be seen, but, at that moment, it seemed as though the curtains were descending gracefully on the intermission after three wonderfully eventful years of our life on the beautiful *Ynys Môn,* or Isle of Anglesey.

To be continued.

Next in the Toad's Adventures Series:

Toads in a Hole

Country Recipes

Honey-Roasted Carrots

2 tablespoons olive or sunflower oil

1 tablespoon honey

1 teaspoon readymade mustard

18 ounces/500 grams carrots peeled and cut into sticks

Method

1. Place the carrots in a covered oven proof pan.
2. Gently melt together the oil, honey, and mustard in a saucepan, stirring until dissolved.
3. Pour the liquid over the carrots and toss to cover them completely.
4. Bake for 20 minutes in an oven, preheated to 180°C/360°F
5. Remove the cover and continue to bake for another 10 minutes.

Roast Hogget

1 leg or forequarter of hogget (or mutton)

1 cup olive or sunflower oil

1 small tin (140g) concentrated tomato paste

1 onion

4 garlic cloves

2 level teaspoons curry powder

1 level teaspoon salt

½-teaspoon ground black pepper

Method

1. Put a large pan on the hot plate with medium heat (cast iron casserole is best).
2. Add the oil, garlic, onion, salt, pepper and curry powder and fry gently with frequent stirring until the onion changes colour.

3. Add the tomato paste and continue to fry with frequent stirring for 2 to 3 minutes, then add the hogget and cover with water.
4. Put the lid on and simmer gently for 2 to 3 hours.
5. Gently transfer the hogget to a roasting tray and cook in the oven at 180°C/360°F for 30–40 minutes.
6. Use some of the liquid in the casserole to make the gravy.
7. Serve with greens, roast potatoes, parsnips, and honey-roasted carrots (see above).
8. Use the remainder of the liquid and any leftovers as a casserole for the next day.

Sausage and Apple Plait
Shortcrust Pastry
12 ounces/300 grams plain flour
½-level teaspoon salt
6 ounces/150 butter or lard
Cold water to mix

Filling
1 lb/450 grams sausage meat
1 onion
1 teaspoon mixed herbs
1 cup of dried breadcrumbs
4 ounces/ 110 grams smoked bacon chopped into small cubes
1 cooking apple, peeled and chopped into small cubes
Salt and pepper to taste

Method
Pastry
1. Sift flour and salt into a bowl.
2. Cut butter into small cubes and cut into flour with a blunt knife, then 'rub in' with fingertips until it resembles fine breadcrumbs.

3. Sprinkle the water over the crumbs and mix to a stiff paste with the knife.
4. Draw together with fingertips then knead until smooth on a lightly floured board.
5. Return to the bowl, cover and refrigerate for 10 minutes.
6. Roll out into an oblong shape, place on a buttered baking tray.

Filling

1. Gently fry the onions and bacon in a little oil.
2. Add to a mixing bowl with all the other ingredients and mix well.
3. Arrange the mixture down the middle third of the rolled-out pastry.
4. Slice the two outer edges of the pastry in opposing diagonal cuts with spacing of about 1 inch/2.5 cm (/// \\\), leaving flaps of 2 inches/5cm, top and bottom.
5. Fold in the top and bottom flaps; moisten the cut edges with a little water and plait all the way down.
6. Brush with milk or beaten egg and bake in the centre of a preheated oven for one hour at 180°C/360°F, or until the pastry is crisp and golden.

Nettle Soup

100 washed young stinging nettle tips (use gloves!)
2lb/900 grams potatoes peeled and cut into bite-sized pieces
1 onion, chopped
Shreds of fresh ginger to taste
4 garlic cloves finely chopped
2 chicken stock cubes
3½ pints/2 litres water
Salt and pepper to taste

Method

1. Lightly fry the potatoes in oil in a pot large enough to hold all the ingredients.
2. Add the onion and ginger and fry gently until a little caramelised, then briefly sauté the garlic.
3. Pour in the water and add the nettle tips.
4. Bring to the boil and boil for 15 minutes.
5. Blend the stock cubes with a cup full of the liquor and then stir into the pot with the remaining potatoes.
6. Season to taste; boil until the potatoes are cooked, but still firm.

Farmhouse Bread Rolls.

2 ounces/50 grams fresh or 2 teaspoons dried yeast

1 teaspoon of sugar

1½ pints/900 ml *warm* water, not hot!

2 lbs/900 grams of strong white bread flour

1 lb/ 450 grams of wholemeal bread flour

2 teaspoons of salt

Olive or sunflower oil

Extra flour to dust the work surface

Method

1. Pour ¼ pint/150 ml of the warm water into a jug and stir in the yeast and sugar.
2. Cover and leave in a warm place to ferment until a foam appears on the top; about 10 minutes.
3. Oil the inside of a warmed mixing bowl; stir in the yeast mixture, salt and the rest of the warm water.
4. Gradually fold in the flour, then knead in the bowl, adding more flour if necessary, until the sides of the bowl are clean.
5. Oil the dough and the inside of the bowl, cover and leave in a warm place until double the size (about an hour).
6. Tip the dough onto a floured board and knead for 5 minutes.

7. Divide into 16 pieces, knead each into the required shape and place onto an oiled baking tray, allowing sufficient room for expansion.
8. Oil the tops and leave to rise for about an hour. (Be careful not to knock the trays, as the dough will go flat.)
9. Bake in a preheated oven, 220°C/425°F for 20 minutes, or longer for a crispy roll. The rolls should slide easily off the baking tray if they have finished cooking and will sound hollow when tapped on the underside.
10. Cool on a wire rack.

Bumper Cars

2 ounces/50 grams fresh yeast or 2 teaspoons dried yeast
4 ounces/110 grams sugar
1½ pints/900 ml *warm* water, not hot!
3 lbs/1360 grams strong white bread flour
8 ounces/220 grams sultanas
1/2 teaspoon salt
Olive or sunflower oil
Extra flour to dust the work surface

Method
1. Pour ¼ pint/150 ml of the warm water into a jug and stir in the yeast and 2 teaspoons of the sugar
2. Cover and leave in a warm place to ferment until a foam appears on the top. (About 10 minutes)
3. Oil the inside of a warmed mixing bowl, pour in the remaining warm water, add the sugar, salt and sultanas and stir in the fermented yeast mixture.
4. Gradually fold in the flour and knead, adding more flour if necessary, until the sides of the bowl are clean.
5. Oil the dough and the inside of the bowl, cover and leave in a warm place until double the size. (About an hour.)

6. Tip the dough onto a floured board and knead for 5 minutes.
7. Divide into 16 pieces, knead each into a sausage shape and place onto an oiled baking tray, reasonably close together so they keep their shape as they rise.
8. Oil the tops and leave to rise for about an hour. (Be careful not to jog the trays, or the dough will go flat!)
9. Bake in a preheated oven, 220°C/425°F for 20 minutes. The rolls should slide easily off the baking tray if they have finished cooking and will sound hollow when tapped on the underside.
10. Cool completely on a wire rack.

Icing

4 ounces/110 grams of icing sugar
Red food colouring
A little boiling water
Hundreds and thousands

Method
1. Put icing sugar into a bowl and drip the boiling water in, one drop at a time, mixing until it is reasonably thick, but still pourable and drizzle along the tops of half of the sweet rolls.
2. Add a few drops of the red food colouring to the remaining icing, mix well and spread along the tops of the remaining rolls.
3. Decorate with the Hundreds and thousands.

Chocolate Beetroot Cake

10 ounces / 280 grams self-raising flour
3 level tablespoons cocoa powder
2 teaspoons baking powder
7 ounces / 200 grams raw, peeled and grated beetroot
4 ounces / 110 grams butter
3 beaten eggs

1 tablespoon golden syrup or honey
½-pint / 300 ml milk
6 ounces / 170 grams sugar
1 teaspoon vanilla essence

Method

1. Into a large mixing bowl, sieve together the flour, cocoa, and baking powder.
2. In a large saucepan, warm the milk, butter and syrup/honey and sugar, and stir until butter melts. Remove from heat and leave to cool completely
3. Pre-heat oven to 160°C/320°F
4. Beat the eggs and vanilla essence into the liquid
5. Stir in the grated beetroot and then the dry ingredients. Mix well.
6. Turn mixture into a greased and lined 8 inch/20cm cake tin and bake for 60-75 minutes or until a metal skewer comes out clean.
7. When completely cool, turn out of the tin, cut in half horizontally and ice the top and inside with chocolate icing.

Chocolate Icing:

9 ounces / 250 grams mascarpone or cream cheese
7 ounces / 200 grams white or dark chocolate
1 heaped tablespoon of marmalade, raspberry jam, or lemon curd
Chopped nuts, grated coconut or lemon peel to decorate

Method

1. Break the chocolate into a large heatproof bowl and allow it to melt slightly over a pan of boiling water.
2. Remove from the boiling water as soon as it begins to melt and stir gently until fully melted.
3. Stir in the marmalade, jam, or lemon curd (optional).
4. Whisk in the mascarpone or cream cheese until well blended.

5. Spread immediately on the inner layer and the top of the cake and sprinkle over desired decoration.
6. Cover and chill.

Boiled Fruit Cake

150g/5oz mixed dried fruit

The grated rind of one orange

250ml/ 8 fluid ounces water

115g/ 4oz dark brown sugar and extra sugar to sprinkle over the top

115g/4oz butter or oil

1 heaped tablespoon golden syrup or honey

225g/8oz self-raising flour

2 teaspoons baking powder

3 beaten eggs

115g/4oz chopped, roasted almonds

Extra whole almonds to decorate

3 tsp mixed spice

1 teaspoon vanilla or almond essence

90ml/ 3 fluid ounces sweet sherry, rum, brandy or orange juice

Method

1. In a bowl, pour the sherry, rum, brandy or orange juice over the fruit, cover and soak overnight.
2. In a large saucepan, combine the fruit, water, sugar, syrup, molasses or honey and butter/oil and stir gently over a medium heat.
3. Cover and simmer for 3 minutes. Remove from heat, and allow to cool completely.
4. Stir in the eggs and the essence.
5. Preheat oven to 180°C/360°F.
6. Line a baking tin of appropriate size with baking paper, allowing room for rising.

7. Stir sifted flour, mixed spice and baking powder into the cool fruit mixture. Add the chopped almonds and orange peel, mix well and pour into prepared baking tin.
8. Decorate cake with carefully arranged whole almonds and sprinkle extra sugar lightly over the top.
9. Bake in the centre of the oven for 60-75 minutes or until a metal skewer pushed into the cake comes out clean.
10. Allow to cool completely.
11. Turn out, wrap and store, preferably in the fridge.

Toffee Popcorn.

   3½ ounces/100 grams popping corn
   2 tablespoons sunflower oil

Toffee coating

   1½ ounces/40 grams soft brown sugar
   4 tablespoons golden syrup or honey
   1 ounce/30 grams butter
   Pinch of salt
   Small bowl of cold water for testing

Method

1. Heat the oil over a medium heat in a large pan with a lid.
2. Add the corn, swirl it all together and cover.
3. After about a minute of popping, lift the pan from the heat, shake it briefly and return to the heat.
4. Repeat this procedure every minute until the popping sound begins to slow down. (Be careful that the corn does not burn)
5. Empty the popped corn into a large bowl, carefully leaving the un-popped kernels in the pan to be discarded. (We do not need any broken teeth here!)
6. Wipe out the pan, return it to the heat and add the butter, syrup/honey, sugar and salt.
7. Stir constantly, dropping a small drop of the mixture into the

bowl of cold water to test the set until a crisp toffee is produced. It should be a light, golden colour.

8. Switch off the heat, add all the popped corn and fold in swiftly, until thoroughly coated with the toffee.
9. Toss out onto a lightly buttered baking tray to cool.
10. Gently break apart the toffee popcorn before it cools completely and serve.

Nettle Ginger Beer.

100 young stinging nettle tips

1 gallon/4.5 litres water

1 lb/450 grams sugar

1 lemon, sliced

1 ounce/ 28 grams fresh or 2 teaspoons dried yeast

2 teaspoons ground ginger

Method

1. Put the sugar into a large, lidded container.
2. Boil the nettle tips in the water for 15 minutes, then strain onto the sugar and discard the nettles or use them for nettle soup.
3. Stir the sugar-water until thoroughly dissolved.
4. Cool until tepid, then add the ground ginger, sliced lemon and yeast.
5. Cover and stir daily for one week before use.

Spiced Beetroot Wine

1 Gallon/4.5 litres Water

4lb/1.8 Kg beetroot

3lb/1.4 Kg sugar

Juice and thinly peeled rind of one lemon (discard the pith and pips)

4-6 whole cloves

½ ounce / 14 grams root ginger, peeled and finely sliced.

½ ounce / 14 grams baker's yeast or one teaspoon dried yeast

Method

1. Pour the sugar into a large, clean, lidded plastic bucket.
2. Wash the beetroot well, cut into thin slices, put into a large pan with some of the water. Add lemon peel, cloves and ginger.
3. Bring to the boil, simmer until the beetroot is tender and has lost colour.
4. Strain onto the sugar and stir well until all the sugar is dissolved then add the remaining water. Discard solids.
5. Leave to cool until lukewarm then take some of the liquid in a jug and mix with yeast.
6. Stir into the bucket along with lemon juice.
7. Cover the bucket and leave in a warm place for 2 days to start fermentation.
8. Decant into glass fermentation bottles (demijohns) and insert airlocks. Leave in a warm place until fermentation has finished and sediment has formed on the bottom.
9. Syphon off into glass bottles, being careful to leave sediment in fermentation bottles.
10. Firmly cork, label and store in a cool, dark location.

Meadowsweet Champagne

10 large flower heads of Meadowsweet in full bloom

1 gallon/4.5 litres water

2 lb/450 grams sugar or a little more for extra sweetness

2 lemons, sliced

Method

1. Put the sugar into a large, lidded container. Boil the water, pour over the sugar and stir until dissolved.
2. Allow to cool then add the sliced lemons.

3. Carefully trim the flowers off the stalks and sprinkle them onto the brew. Leave to blend for 24 hours then strain into strong beer bottles and firmly secure.
4. Drink chilled and open with care. Extremely lively after three weeks, potent and mellow after nine months.

Glossary of Welsh Names, Words and Expressions

Aber	---	Estuary
Afon	---	River
Arglwydd	---	Lord (dd is pronounced as th)
Bach/Fach	---	Small
Badrig/Padrig	---	Patrick
Bara Brith	---	Dried fruit bread
Bod	---	Dwelling
Bore da	---	Good morning
Bryn	---	Hill
Bryn Awel	---	Breezy Hill
Bryn Llyn	---	Hill by the Lake
Cae	---	Field, enclosure
Caer/Din	---	Fort
Capel	---	Chapel
Carreg	---	Stone
Cerrig	---	Stones
Cefn	---	Ridge
Coch/Goch	---	Red
Coed/Coeden	---	Trees/tree
Craig	---	Rock
Croes	---	Cross
Cymraeg	---	Welsh Language
Dau	---	Two
Dawel	---	Still, quiet, silent
Dewch yma	---	Come here
Dim ots	---	It does not matter
Dre/Tre	---	Town
Dri/Tri	---	Three

Du	---	Black
Duw	---	God
Dŵr	---	Water
Eglwys	---	Church
Ewch lawr	---	Go/get down
Fawr	---	Big
Ffordd	---	Road/way (ff is pronounced as F)
Ffynnon	---	Well
Glas	---	Blue
Gorsedd	---	Throne
Gwylfa	---	Lookout
Gwyrdd	---	Green
Hafod	---	Summerhouse/Dairy
Llan	---	Church
Llyn	---	Lake
Maes	---	Field
Mechell/Fechell		A 6th Century Saint
Melin/Felin	---	Mill
Mynydd	---	Mountain
Na	---	Not/no/do not
Panad	---	Cuppa/ cup of tea
Pandy	---	Fulling mill
Pant	---	Hollow or valley
Pen	---	Head or top
Pethau da	---	Sweets/good things
Prynhawn da	---	Good afternoon
Porth	---	Port
Post Brenhinol	---	Royal Mail
Rhos	---	Heath or moor
Rhyd	---	Ford
Saesneg	---	English
Saith Môr	---	Seven Seas

Siarad	---	Speak
Sut ydych chi?	---	How are you?
Tan	---	Under
Tir	---	Land
Traeth	---	Beach
Trefor	---	Trevor (single f is pronounced as v)
Tri	---	Three
Tros	---	Over
Trwyn	---	Point
Tŷ	---	House
Tŷn	---	Small Farm
Tŷn Llain	---	House on a plot, or long strip of land
Tyddyn	---	Smallholding
Uchaf	---	Upper
Un	---	One
Wela i chi	---	See you later
Wen	---	White
Y/Yr	---	The
Ynys	---	Island
Ysbyty	---	Hospital

Tŷn Llain Bed & Breakfast

TYN LLAIN B&B

Come and enjoy a peaceful break nestled in rural Anglesey just 10 minutes from the sea.

BOOK DIRECTLY via our website:

www.tynllainbandb.com.

Made in the USA
Monee, IL
18 February 2024

53739784R00193